SO-AXB-722

by
Hollis Lee

Countryside
Books

Preface

If you own a few acres or plan to acquire a country place, you probably know about the rich rewards associated with country living: the open space, the fresh air, the chance to do some real farming, gardening and animal raising on your own land.

We have published this series of **Country Home & Small Farm Guides** *to provide the basics you'll need to succeed in a broad range of projects and activities on two acres or 100.*

We realize that for most people country living is a very private pursuit. After all, a big part of its appeal is not having to look into the next guy's window when you look out of yours. But we hope you will communicate with us. Tell us how you like our books, share bits of country wisdom and suggest additional subjects or services we can provide.

Contents

Illustrations by Wayne Kibar

ISBN 0-88453-031-0

©1978 by Countryside Books
A.B. Morse Company, 200 James Street, Barrington, IL 60010

Printed in U.S.A.

Introduction

4

Nuts and fruits and berries are foods that will improve your diet and increase the appeal of your roadside market. Because of their numerous varieties, you are bound to find at least one variety of each that will grow in your area.

This book contains specific information about planning and preparation, planting, pruning, training, soil management, propagating, pollination, harvesting, insects and diseases, and varieties. These data, along with consultation with your local county agent concerning local problems, should help you successfully raise nuts and fruits and berries.

Nut Trees

The value of nut trees cannot be measured in dollars alone. While they can become a source of extra income when harvested in large quantities, on a smaller scale they can provide many pounds of nuts for the family. Almost anyone would appreciate having a readily available supply of walnuts or pecans for baking purposes, especially during the winter holiday season.

Nuts are an important but often overlooked food source. They are high in protein, fat, minerals and some vitamins, but they are also higher in calories than most foods. They can grow on land that is not adequate for other food production. This feature will probably increase their value as a food in view of the growing world population. Stony land or slopes too steep for cultivated crops are usable if the soil is moderately fertile and well drained. Areas subject

Nut trees can be productive when planted along fences, using land often taken over by weeds.

5

to intermittent flooding, although not suitable for cultivated crops, can be very good for growing nut trees because of the excellent soil. Even when this land is used for pasture, nut trees can be grown if protected from livestock when the trees are young. Nut trees have been very productive when planted along stream beds and fence rows. Such land, usually taken over by weed trees and scrub brush, might as well grow productive nut trees.

There are other values to be gained from planting nut trees around your country place. Wherever shade trees are wanted near farm buildings and country homes, nut trees may very well be the first choice; in fact, they equal or surpass many ornamental trees that are planted for shade, and they almost always lend an aesthetic beauty to the surroundings. Pecans, hickories and walnuts are among the best large shade trees. Some varieties of these species can be grown almost anywhere in the United States. It is just a matter of wedding the location and variety together.

Nut trees will produce valuable nut crops during their early vigorous years and valuable timber when they are old. For example, black walnut timber is highly prized for making fine furniture, for interior furnishings and for gunstocks. Because this wood

*Some nut woods
are used for
furniture and
gun stocks.*

6

is becoming rare, its value is increasing. Pecan is also used for making furniture and for flooring, and is sometimes used for smoking meats.

In some areas nut trees grown under intensive management on good crop land are a very profitable crop. However, such areas are very limited and require a considerable investment in both time and money. Depending on the species and varieties, it will take from 5 to 10 years before the nut trees become established enough to make a commercial crop.

Remember that nut trees should receive special attention until they have become well established. Don't think that nut trees do not require care because they grow wild. You should study available information on nut tree culture if you want your trees to produce well.

Walnuts

Varieties of the walnut tree can be found all over the United States. This section describes some of the growing conditions and varieties of three well-known members of the walnut family.

Black Walnuts

The black walnut *(Juglans nigra)* is the most widely grown nut tree in the United States. Black walnuts are cultivated in some part of almost every state in this country. Although it grows naturally in 32 states, the black walnut grows most abundantly in the 12 Central States. Most of the nut production is from the wild trees that grow on non-crop land.

Proper selection of varieties is the key to raising black walnuts for nut production. Improved varieties, or cultivars, have been planted throughout the country with varying degrees of success.

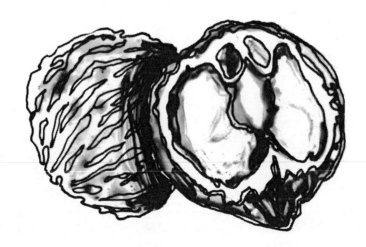

Cultivars originating in a specific region are best adapted to that region. For example, cultivars that do well in the northern areas seldom do well in the southern areas, and vice versa. Use caution when planting any cultivar in the extreme limits of the natural range. Selections of local origin normally perform better than listed popular cultivars from more distant areas.

Planning and preparation

Select planting locations for black walnuts with care. The tree requires a deep, well-drained, fertile soil with an ample supply of moisture. Good locations may be found near the barn or house; however, some home owners do not like them in the yard because they litter hulls, nuts and leaves in the fall. Farmers rate the tree as ideal in permanent pastures, along stream beds, and in odd corners of fields. Livestock like the shade it provides. For good growth and nut production, the tree should be at least 50 feet away from other trees. Try to keep the young plants protected from livestock and farm equipment.

Planting

Follow the procedure below when planting black walnut trees.

1. Purchase and set out the tree in late winter or early spring.
2. Be sure that the roots on the trees do not dry out before planting.

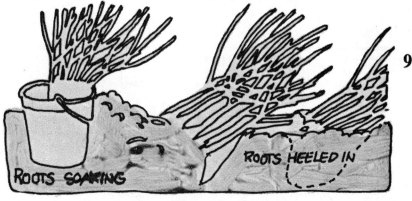

ROOTS SOAKING

ROOTS HEELED IN

Planting
Nut
Trees

PRUNE ROOTS
ABOVE BREAK

BREAK

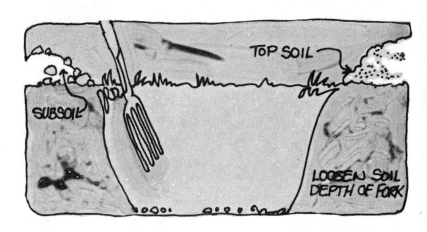

TOP SOIL

SUBSOIL

LOOSEN SOIL
DEPTH OF FORK

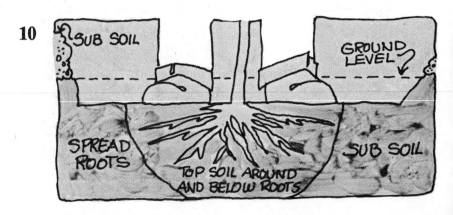

SUB SOIL

GROUND
LEVEL

SPREAD
ROOTS

TOP SOIL AROUND
AND BELOW ROOTS

SUB SOIL

3. Dig the planting hole deep enough to set the tree at the same depth it was growing in the nursery.
4. Prune the roots to fit the hole without crowding.
5. Where possible, mix some river sand with the dirt that was removed from the hole and add enough water to insure that there are no air pockets remaining around the roots.
6. Tamp the fill in around the tree firmly.

Training

During the first years after planting, train the tree to a single stem. A little corrective training early prevents a misshapen tree and produces a tree that later has a higher value.

Soil management

Do not fertilize the young tree the first year it is set out. After that, fertilize the tree with one pound of 5-10-5 (or equal) for each 1 inch of diameter of the tree. Do not fertilize if good growth is obtained without it.

Do not use walnut hulls as mulch in gardens or around flowers. Apple trees, tomatoes, potatoes and other plants can be killed, or at least damaged, from a toxic substance in the hulls and roots of the black walnut.

Pollination

Because the black walnut is late leafing out in the spring, it very seldom suffers frost damage. Flowering is also late, beginning about the same time as leafing or shortly after.

Male and female flowers are borne on the same tree. The male flowers are in catkins, which develop from auxiliary buds of leaves of the previous season's growth. The female flower is borne on the terminals of current growth. This is where the nut develops.

The black walnut tree is self-fertilizing; however, cross pollination is desirable because the sequence of the male and female blooming, called *dichogamy,* can and often does have a gap that will cause the tree not to pollinate its own nutlets. In some instances, the time of pollen shedding precedes the receptivity period of the female flower; at other times, pollen may not be shed until after pistil receptivity. Different varieties have different blossoming times, so planting more than one variety tends to assure nut production.

Varieties

There are hundreds of black walnut cultivars, but those most often produced by nut tree nurseries are the Hare, Myer, Ohio, Stabler, Thomas and Victoria. That certain ones are not catalogued does not mean they lack superiority. Commercial nurseries grow the ones that the public is most familiar with and those with established performance records. The following is a brief description of these varieties based on nut quality, planting performance and characteristics.

1. **Hare.** Origin Illinois. Nut is heavy with good kernel weight. On a par with Thomas. Propagates easily by budding and is above average in plant survival. Well adapted to Illinois and surrounding areas.

2. **Myer.** Origin Ohio. Has very thin shell and good cracking qualities. Very vigorous, upright tree. Yields good nuts regularly. Well adapted to eastern and northeastern U.S.

3. **Ohio.** Origin Ohio. Excellent total kernel percentage. Vigorous, upright tree. Yields regular crops of good quality. Has shown exceptional survival in plantings.

4. **Stabler.** Origin Maryland. Has a very thin shell. Nut production has been variable. Good producer on the east coast.

5. **Thomas.** Origin Pennsylvania. Has high kernel weight and percentage. Has become a well-known black walnut cultivar. Often used as a standard for comparison. Vigorous, early bearing tree, but sometimes tends to bear alternately. Adapted to wider areas than most.

6. **Victoria.** Origin Kentucky. Vigorous tree. Resistant to leaf spot. Tends to bear alternately. Has thicker shells than most.

Persian Walnuts

The Persian walnut *(Juglans regia)* can be found growing wild in an area extending from the Carpathian Mountains across Turkey, Iraq, Iran and southern Russia. This family has several varieties, the most common being the English walnut, the Carpathian walnut, and the variety called Persian walnut. Each variety is grown in a different climate.

The French varieties grown on the West Coast are commonly known as Persian walnuts. These varieties are least cold tolerant of the *Juglans regia.* They are not adapted to the eastern United States or to high mountain climates. They are generally restricted to the coastal areas, interior valleys and foothills, and areas west of the Sierra Nevada and Cascade Mountains. A few Persian walnuts are being grown in southwest Arizona.

The Persian walnut needs long, warm and generally dry summers. In areas with cool summers, the nut kernel percentage is low. However, a certain amount of winter chilling is needed to break the rest or dormancy, so that the tree will start growth and bloom in the spring.

Persian walnuts make good dooryard trees in the areas to which they are adapted.

Carpathian Walnuts

The Carpathian walnut is the cold-hardy variety of the Persian walnut *(Juglans regia)*. The most successful plantings are near 40° latitude. The term Carpathian walnut includes all hardy Persian walnuts from Ukraine, Russia, Czechoslovakia and Germany. **13**

The Carpathian walnut tree is an excellent dooryard tree, because it is smooth and symmetrical. The rather deeply seated branching roots do not srongly compete with lawn grasses for moisture and nutrients or with other woody plants in nearby locations. The Carpathian walnut is a relatively "clean" tree in the yard.

The Carpathian walnut grows and produces in the northeastern United States and the North Central States, including the southern part of Canada. When fully dormant, many varieties can withstand low winter temperatures of –35° to –40°F. Sudden temperature changes in late winter or early spring can cause trunk damage. The majority of the varieties are early vegetators, and crops may be lost to early spring freezes. Also, unless they receive sufficient summer heat, the nuts may not fill out and the kernel will be shrunken.

Planting

The Carpathian walnut should be planted in the same manner and should receive the same type of treatment as the black walnut.

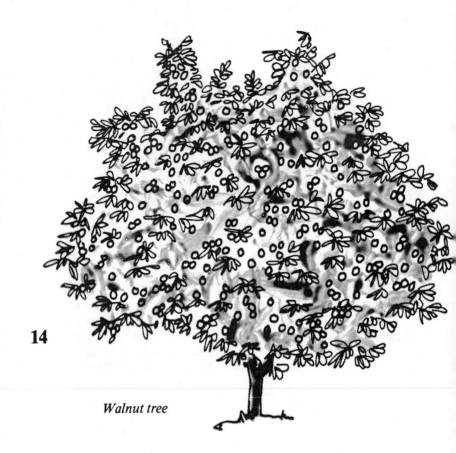

Walnut tree

Varieties

Several clones have been selected for their superior quality to establish varieties.

The varieties described below are the ones that are most likely to be available in the nurseries. This does not mean that other varieties are not as good or as well adapted.

1. **Hansen.** Believed to be of German origin. A relatively small tree. An annual bearer of small, thin-shelled nuts, 60% kernels. Self-pollinating, winter-hardy and adapted to a wide range of site conditions. May be damaged by late freezes in the spring.

2. **Metcalfe.** An annual bearer of good quality nuts, 52% kernels. Winter-hardy in northern New York state.

3. **Fickes.** Medium-sized nuts, 51% kernels. Adapted to Illinois and Iowa.

4. **Somers.** Medium-sized nuts, 48% kernels. One of the earliest ripening varieties. Matures early. Suited for areas having short or cool summers.

5. **Broadview.** Imported from Odessa, Russia. Probably the highest producer of any variety. An annual bearer with a long, oval shell, 47% kernels. Slightly bitter flavor.

6. **Lake.** Good-sized nut, 50% kernels, good flavor. Yields well in Illinois and Missouri.

7. **McKinster:** Good medium-sized nut, 48% kernels. Self-pollinating. Favored in Ohio and Michigan.

Pecans

The pecan *(Carya illinoensis)* is an excellent food. Almost without exception everyone enjoys eating pecans. In addition to being eaten raw or roasted, they are used extensively in cooking. The mature kernel consists of approximately 72% oil, 11% protein, 13% carbohydrates, 3% moisture and 1% ash. There are also 3,630 calories in a pound of pecan kernels.

Approximately 205 million pounds of nuts are produced every year in the United States. Because the demand is steadily increasing both for local consumption and for export, markets exist almost everywhere for surplus pecans. They also make an excellent addition to the roadside market. There are cases where three or four

pecan trees have produced enough income to pay the property taxes each year.

The nomad Indian tribes were known to time their treks so they would arrive at wild pecan groves in early autumn to take advantage of the nut crops. The pecan nuts served as an important food source in their diets. The name pecan comes from an Indian word *pacanes,* which means "a hard nut to crack."

The pecan tree is native to a wide area of Texas, Oklahoma, Arkansas, Louisiana and Mississippi. To a lesser extent, it is also native to Kansas, Missouri, Tennessee, Kentucky, Indiana, Illinois, Iowa and Nebraska. The cultural range of pecans overlaps the native range and extends westward into New Mexico, Arizona and California. In the West they must be irrigated to produce nuts. They are also grown in the southeastern states of Georgia, Florida, Alabama and South Carolina.

The pecan makes an excellent shade or ornamental tree in addition to its nut production. Different cultivars have distinctive growth habits ranging from upright to low spreading. Pecan trees can also be pruned and shaped.

Planning and Preparation

Temperature

The pecan requires a long, frost-free period from the time growth starts in the spring until the nuts mature in the fall. It grows best where the summer temperature is from 75° to 85°F without too much variation between day and night. The number of growing days varies with the cultivars and ranges from 150 to 210 days. Pecans are classified as northern cultivars and southern cultivars. The classification is based primarily on the number of days growth required for the nuts to reach maturity.

The new growth on pecan trees is very sensitive to frost. Even though the tree is late in leafing out in the spring, frost damage does occur. If your area is noted for late freezes and frost, choose a cultivar that is later than normal in starting spring growth.

Humidity

Pecan trees grow in areas with high relative humidity. However, when the humidity exceeds about 80%, pollination becomes a problem because the anthers do not open properly. Also trees in high humidity areas are more susceptible to disease and insect damage. Only trees that are at least tolerant of or resistant to scab disease should be planted in high humidity areas.

Rainfall

If you live in an area with less than 35 inches of rain, you will need to irrigate to grow satisfactory nut crops. In the summer, the pecan tree requires about 1 inch of rainfall each week, supplied either from reserves in the soil or by irrigation. In the early fall, the tree needs adequate moisture to properly mature the nuts. For the first couple of years after the trees are set out, be sure they receive adequate moisture.

Soil

Good, deep, well-drained soil is ideal for growing pecans; but they will grow on almost any type of soil ranging from alkaline to acid. Soil depth is important, because pecans grow to be very large trees, some as tall as 160 or 170 feet with trunk diameters reaching 4 to 6 feet near the ground. Because of their size and longevity, they need a firm anchor in the soil, as well as a reservoir for storage of water and plant food. Pecan trees cannot tolerate a high water table, so avoid planting on swampy or poorly drained soils.

Planting

Planting plan

Make a planting plan before ordering trees so that you can order the correct number of each variety. The plan should insure adequate, but not surplus, space for the trees. In making the plan, consider economical use of the land, the time required to obtain commercial yields, soil type, water systems, and spacing. You need a planting plan even if you want to plant only a few trees around the house, outbuildings or fence rows, or in idle corners in the fields.

Three basic planting plans for orchards exist:
1 — conventional spacing with intercropping,
2 — conventional spacing with filler trees,
3 — high-density spacing.

The conventional spacings are 100 x 100, 80 x 80, 60 x 60, and 50 x 50 with variations of these numbers. These spacings waste land unless temporary crops are grown between the trees until they begin to fill the space after a few years' growth. The open land can be used for pasture, but each individual tree should be protected by a structure such as a three-sided fence.

The use of filler trees is losing favor because of the increased cost of establishing an orchard. With this plan, excess trees are planted initially and removed as the pecan trees grow in size.

The newest concept is high-density spacings of 25 x 25, 30 x 30, or 40 x 40 with such variations as 17.5 x 35 and 40 x 20. Varieties used for this type of planting must be capable of being pruned or hedged to maintain tree size to let in adequate sunlight and prevent overcrowding. Some of the cultivars showing promise for high-density plantings are Cape Fear, Chickasaw, Cherokee, Tejas and Wichita. With such close spacing, irrigation is almost a must.

19

Pecan tree

Preparing to plant

Pecan trees shed leaves and begin dormancy in October and November, depending upon the area. They can be dug and transplanted after this. The best season for transplanting, however, is in late winter or early spring as the buds begin to swell. Be forewarned that a transplanted pecan tree has a rendezvous with death and will require a lot of attention.

If the nursery from which you purchase the trees offers root treatment with indole -3- butic acid (IBA), take advantage of it. This treatment helps produce fibrous roots, which are necessary for survival and normal growth.

If you are planning an orchard, use the following procedure:

1. Clear the land of all other trees, shrubs and vegetation.
2. Plow and disk the soil as if you were planting a regular crop.
3. Be sure the site drains well.
4. Install irrigation pipe and/or ditches prior to planting the trees.
5. Stake the site to indicate the location of each tree. Many planters color code the stakes to indicate what variety is to be planted at each stake. There is less confusion at planting time when a color code system is used.

Planting the trees

1. Dig the planting holes with an 8 to 12-inch tractor-mounted post hole auger, or by hand, to a depth that will accommodate the root system of the tree to be planted.
2. Prune the roots to fit the hole. Do not crowd the roots in the hole.
3. Unless the soil is a good sandy loam, mix sand with the soil that was removed from the hole. As a general rule, a 50-50 mixture should be used.
4. Set the tree in the hole to about its original depth.
5. Backfill the soil firmly in the hole. Use plenty of water; rod to be sure that all air pockets are removed from around the roots.
6. Do not use fertilizer when transplanting or for the first growing season.

20

Pruning

After planting, prune the tops of the trees back 1/3 to 1/2 their original length. Make the cuts 2 to 3 inches above a bud facing the direction of the prevailing wind. Wrap the trunk for 12 to 18 inches with aluminum foil or brown crepe paper. For the next 2 or 3 years, prune the tops to produce a single trunk 5 to 7 feet high with wide angle crotches. Narrow-angled V or Y crotches are weak and objectionable.

Flowering and Pollination

The flowering habit of the pecan is similar to that of the black walnut. The staminate, the male flower that produces the pollen necessary for setting fruit, is borne on catkins, which are formed in lateral buds of 1-year-old shoots. Catkins formed in buds during one season complete their development and shed pollen early in the following season's growth. A single catkin produces over 2.5 million pollen grains; only one grain is required for each pecan. A bearing tree produces several thousand catkins, all of which are needed because the pecan relies on gravity and wind to move the pollen to the pistillate flower. Bees and other insects do not help pollinate pecans. Heavy rains at the time the catkins shed the pollen can wash the pollen from the trees and cause a poor nut set.

The pistillate is the female flower that develops into the pecan nut. The shoot that develops it is formed in the early spring. This is in contrast with the catkin, which is formed in the summer several months before it completes its development early the following spring. By the time the pistillate can be seen, the shoot which it terminates usually will have grown to 6 or 8 inches.

The receptive period of the pistil is indicated by a change of the stigma from a deep green to a light yellow color. Some cultivars develop a tinge of red around the edge of the stigma as it becomes receptive. A pollen grain that falls on the stigma germinates and fertilizes the egg. Pistillate flowers that are not fertilized dry up and fall from the tree in about 5 weeks after they are receptive.

21

The period when the catkin sheds pollen and when the stigma is receptive may or may not be the same on the tree. This depends upon the cultivar (variety) and the weather conditions. In some cultivars the stigma is receptive before the pollen is shed; in others the pollen is shed before the stigma is receptive. Thus, pecan plantings should always consist of at least one protandrous variety (pollen shed before stigma is receptive), and one protogynous variety (stigma receptive before pollen is shed). Plant the trees selected for pollinators around the edges of the orchard, particularly on the side from which the prevailing winds blow.

Pecans on tree
ready for harvest

Harvesting

Pecans are harvested in the fall beginning in October and continuing until after the first of the year. Some large pecan growers have mechanical harvesting equipment; however, small orchards are usually harvested by hand. Thresh the trees by knocking or flailing the nuts from the tree; then pick them up by hand. Keep the different varieties separate at harvest. Store the pecans in a cool, dry place until marketed.

Given the usual care and maintenance, a planted orchard of the new varieties will produce a few pecans by the 3rd and 4th years after transplanting with commercial production (25 to 35 pound range) attained by the 7th year. As the trees get older, production will continue to increase. Some native trees over 300 years old have been known to produce a thousand pounds of pecans in one year. Trees that produce a heavy crop in one year usually have a light crop the next year.

Varieties

The selection of varieties is one of the most important decisions that the grower has to make. The expense and the time for growing the tree are such that it requires careful selection. Several hundred cultivars have been developed over the years, but few have shown characteristics so outstanding that they have not been replaced by newer varieties. The Department of Agriculture's Research Service has released several new varieties for propagation. These varieties have Indian tribe names.

The following is a list of some of the more popular varieties being planted throughout the country. Before making any selections, check with local growers and with your county agent.

Apache

Good producer of high quality nuts. 40 to 60 per pound. High kernel percentage of 55 to 60%. Medium maturing. Not scab resistant. Good for western area. Protogynous blooms (flower reception first). Vigorous in growth. Moderately precocious (early bearing).

Barton

Has all-round good qualities. Moderately precocious. Shell unusually thin and well suited for cracking. 45 to 60 nuts per pound. High kernel percentage of 54 to 58%. Tolerant of scab. Protandrous blooming (sheds pollen first). Recommended for Oklahoma because of early nut maturing and late leafing in spring.

Caddo

Small, football-shaped nut. Dark shell. 60 to 75 per pound. Kernel flavor excellent. Scab resistant. Recommended for southern portion of pecan belt. Medium maturing. Protandrous blooming.

Cape Fear
    Originated in North Carolina. Very precocious. Round nut. 40 nuts per pound. Kernel percentage about 52%. Has good disease resistance. Adapted to high-density planting. Protandrous blooming.

Cherokee
    Nuts mature very early, in late September or early October. One of the most precocious and prolific bearing varieties. Good for high-density planting. 50 to 70 per pound. Good kernel percentage of 55 to 60%. Not scab resistant. Needs good fungicide spray program in the Southeast. Protandrous blooming.

Cheyenne
    Matures nuts in midseason. 55 to 70 per pound. Very good kernel percentage of 57 to 61%. Very precocious and prolific. Has borne 1.5 pounds of nuts (100 nuts) in the third growing season. Good in high-density plantings. Not scab resistant. Not a good yard tree. Tends to be small. Recommended for the west. Protandrous blooming.

Chickasaw
    Early nut maturity. A small pecan 55 to 75 per pound. Average kernel percentage of 52 to 58%. Very precocious and prolific. Very well suited to high-density planting. Shows good disease resistance. Protandrous blooming.

Choctaw
    Large nut. 40 to 50 per pound. 60% kernels. A fine nut for in-shell trade. High oil content with rich flavor. Comes into production in about 8 years. Recommended for southern areas with spray program. Protandrous blooming.

Commanche
    Large size nuts. 35 to 50 per pound. Good kernel percentage of 52 to 57%. A moderate producer. Good resistance to downy spot and scab. Protogynous blooming.

24

Desirable
    One of the leading commercial varieties in the southeast. Moderately large nut. 43 per pound. Kernel percentage of about 52%. Has good disease resistance. Starts production in about 8 years. Protandrous blooming.

Fritz
    An Illinois seeding. The most northern selection. Strong tree, matures early nuts. Good tree to plant with Witte for pollination. Protandrous blooming.

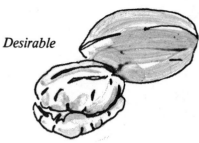

Desirable

Commanche

Majors

25

Mohawk

Wichita

GraBohls

Begins very early to produce heavy crops. Very precocious and prolific. Large nut. 35 to 50 per pound. Very good kernel percentage of 58 to 65%. Large nut clusters on the tree. Needs a good spray program and lots of water. Protandrous blooming.

GraPark Giant

Nuts are among the largest. 25 per pound. Kernel percentage of 52 to 54%. Scab resistant. Has a dark green foliage. Good yard tree.

Mohawk

Large nut. 35 to 50 per pound. Very high shelling percentage, 55 to 60%. High quality nuts. Vigorous tree. Excellent yard tree. Moderately precocious. Should do well in northern areas. Protogynous blooming.

Majors

The standard northern cultivar. 60 to 80 nuts per pound. 42 to 50% kernels. Nut is roundish, but bears well. Protandrous blooming.

Peruque

A Missouri seeding. Good vigor. Bears early and well. Thin shell. Small nut. 60 to 80 per pound. Good kernel percentage of 55 to 63%. Protandrous blooming.

Shoshoni

Released in 1972. Nuts mature early. Medium size. About 60 to the pound. Very vigorous and upright tree, but with strong crotch angles. Highly precocious and very prolific. Suitable for high-density planting. Disease resistant. Because of early ripening, should do well in areas with short growing seasons.

Sioux

Good producer with nuts maturing about midseason. Small nuts. 60 to 80 per pound. High kernel percentage of 58 to 61%. Very high quality kernel — smooth, oily, attractive color and a good flavor. Moderately precocious. Needs spray program. Protogynous blooming.

Tejas

Nuts mature in mid-October. 50 to 70 per pound. Kernel percentage 50 to 56%. A very vigorous and foliated tree. Very precocious and prolific bearer. Ideally suited for both commercial and dooryard planting. Sheds pollen for 18 to 21 days. Excellent pollinator for other varieties. Protogynous blooming. Needs a spray program.

Wichita

Good nuts of 45 to 60 per pound. Very precocious. Bears heavy. Nut generally well filled. Main characteristics include good foliage and early, heavy, consistent yields. Not highly scab resistant. Well suited to high-density planting. Protogynous blooming.

Witte

Small nuts. 60 to 70 per pound. Fair shelling percentage, 44 to 50%. Matures early. Has good shape, blocky. Symmetrical with dense foliage. Good dooryard tree. Iowa seeding, good in northern areas. Protandrous blooming.

Chestnuts

The chestnut is a relative of the oak. Both belong to the cup-bearing trees with the chestnut producing three nuts in each cup.

Chestnuts make excellent dooryard trees. They are available in a wide range of shapes and sizes in the Chinese, Japanese, European or Italian varieties, all of which show resistance to the fungus disease.

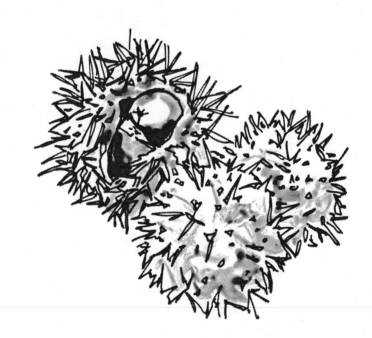

Planning and Preparation

Chestnut trees will grow in almost any area where native hardwood trees grow. However, they do not withstand dry weather very well.

Site location

Plant the chestnut tree on high, sloping ground for adequate air drainage to prevent frost damage.

Soil

Chestnuts prefer a well-drained, sandy loam soil, moderately acid (pH — 5.5 to 6.5).

Fertilizers

Fertilizer should not be used at planting time or during the first year, because it will burn the tree until it develops enough roots to absorb nutrients.

Planting and Pruning

Planting

Plant the chestnut tree in the same manner as the black walnut. You can plant the trees either in the fall or spring in the South, preferably only in the spring in the northern areas. Chestnut trees should be spaced so that the mature tree will have plenty of room. Fifty- to sixty-foot spacing is considered best.

Pruning

As with pecans and walnuts, heavy pruning and topping back are advised at the time of transplanting.

Varieties

The American chestnut was a large spreading tree distributed widely over the eastern United States. It has been virtually eliminated by a fungus disease *(Endothia parasitua),* which was introduced from the Orient in the late 1800s. Only a few trees can be found today. **29**

Chinese chestnuts are presently the favored varieties for orchard nut production. However, several hybrid chestnuts have been developed, including columnar types for dooryard trees and trees that are heavy bearers of small nuts for game. Select varieties such as the following that are resistant to the chestnut blight fungus.

Abundance

Imported from China. Attractive nut with a rich brown color. Excellent flavor. Adapted to Pennsylvania, Ohio, and adjacent areas.

Clapper

A cross between a Chinese and American chestnut. Very fast grower. Good nuts of medium size and color. Adapted over a wide area. Original tree grown at Carbondale, Illinois.

Crane

A Chinese seedling. Nuts are dark cherry-red and almost hairless. Average 32 per pound. Excellent flavor. Early bearer. Extensively planted in the South and Southeast.

Kuling

From Hang Chow, China. Dark brown nuts. Average 35 to 40 per pound. The tree grows more upright than most Chinese chestnut trees. Does well in the South.

Meiling

A Chinese variety, upright in growth habits. The nuts are light tan. Excellent flavor.

Nanking

The most widely planted of the Chinese varieties. Very precocious. Bears heavy crops of nuts. Dark tan in color. Usually 30 to 35 per pound. Adapted to a wide area.

Orrin

A Chinese type developed in Pennsylvania. Nuts are dark mahogany color, almost black, 35 nuts per pound. Superior keeping quality. Early maturing.

Sleeping Giant

A hybrid released by the Connecticut Agricultural Experiment Station in 1960. A consistent producer of large nuts. 40 to the pound. Should make an excellent dooryard tree.

Other Nut Trees

In addition to the more common nut trees described in earlier sections of this book, the following nut trees are also popular. Many can be grown only in certain parts of the country.

Chinkapins

The Chinkapins are of the Chestnut family, and are distinguished by having one nut per bur. Several species grow in the southeastern United States; all are small trees or shrubs. They produce a small nut that has excellent flavor. Very little has been accomplished in trying to produce Chinkapins for commercial marketing.

Filberts

Varieties of filberts are cultivated extensively for nuts on the west coast of Oregon and Washington. They are a small tree that tends to sucker freely. The nuts vary in size according to varieties, the European being considered the best.

American Hazelnut

This tree is a native of North America. It can be grown from Canada to Georgia, Missouri and Oklahoma. The nuts are small and thick shelled. The hazelnut is of the same family as the filbert and will hybridize with the European filbert. The best of the hybrids have nuts as large as the European varieties.

Almonds

The almond is different from the other nut trees in that it is of the botanical family *Rosareae* and related to the peach, plum and apricot. Consequently, the tree and its requirements are more like that of the peach. In fact, breeders are attempting to extend the normal growing regions of the almond to more nearly match that of the peach. At the present time, commercial growing of almonds is limited to certain areas of the West Coast. A few varieties have been released for dooryard planting in other sections of the country. These varieties tend to have a slightly bitter taste. Consider planting commercial orchards only if you are located in an almond producing area.

Macadamia Nuts

The macadamia tree produces a high quality nut. The tree is also used as an ornamental for landscaping around homes. The macadamia tree is an evergreen and is only adapted to the subtropical areas of California, Florida and Hawaii where the nuts are much in demand.

Oaks

The oak trees in the United States produce an annual nut crop (acorns) far greater in yield than all the other nut trees combined. The nut crop is important in furnishing food for game animals and birds. They have very limited use otherwise. Oaks of one kind or another grow in almost all parts of the United States. Several selections are exceptional ornamental trees for dooryard planting.

American Beech

The American beech is native to eastern North America. It grows only as far west as Wisconsin on the northern boundary to east Texas on the southern boundary. The beech is a large tree, and its location is usually known to squirrels and hunters. The nuts are pale brown colored, borne in pairs, and highly prized for their delectable flavor.

Pinyon Pines

Several species of pinyon pines growing in the western states furnish the local inhabitants with a very excellent nut. The nuts are small but highly prized, both for eating raw and in cooked foods.

33

Propagating Nut Trees

If you are just starting out with fruit or nut trees, you will probably purchase your plant stock from a reliable nursery. At some point, however, you might want to experiment with propagation techniques. Budding and grafting are methods of propagating fruit and nut trees so that the trees reproduce true to form. Plants raised from seed seldom, if ever, reproduce fruit equal to the parent tree. Budding and grafting are the only sure way to know what the fruit from the tree will be. This is the way named varieties are reproduced.

Budding

Budding is one way to reproduce fruit and nut trees. With this method, a bud from a known variety is inserted into a seedling (or rootstock) of unknown quality. The rootstock is the vehicle through which the known variety will grow. Normally only one bud is inserted into each rootstock.

When to bud

Budding is usually done in the late summer or early fall when buds of the current season are well formed and the bark slips easily. Buds may be too immature, but seldom are they too mature for successful budding. The bud will start growth early the following spring.

Preparing the budsticks

Budsticks are the shoots of a known variety that carry the buds for budding. You should use the well-developed, plump and hard buds from the midportion of the shoot, discarding the soft tip buds and basal buds.

1. Cut shoots of the current season's growth from either bearing or nursery trees. Bearing trees are better since the quality of the fruit or nut is better.
2. Remove the leaves and keep the budstick moist after it has been cut from the parent tree. This will retard loss of moisture by evaporation from the leaves.

3. Use the buds as soon as possible; however, they can be kept for several days if they are wrapped in a moist cloth and placed in plastic bags.

Preparing the seedling

In early summer, prepare the seedling (rootstock) or limb that is to be budded by stripping off the lateral shoots on the lower 6 inches of the stem. Wipe the stock clean of soil particles near the point of bud insertion. The bud can be inserted by two different methods: the T-cut bud and the patch bud.

Preparing the T-cut bud

1. At budding time, make a T-cut in the bark of the rootstock 2 to 3 inches above the ground or on the limb where the bud is to be inserted.
2. Make the cut through the bark to cambium depth (not into the wood).
3. Some budders prefer to make the transverse cut first, about 1/3 around the stock or about 2 inches on the limb.
4. Then make a vertical cut upward to meet the transverse cut.
5. As the knife reaches the transverse cut, twist the knife blade to raise the edges of the bark just enough, without tearing, so that the bud may be easily inserted.
6. Other budders prefer to make the upward cut first, then the transverse cut.

Preparing the patch bud

The patch bud differs from the T-bud in that two transverse cuts are made parallel to each other about 1 inch apart. They are usually made with a special knife that has the two blades a set distance apart to make both cuts at the same time.

1. Make the horizontal cut with the two-bladed knife.
2. Make the verticle cut from one parallel cut to the other.
3. Twist the knife slightly so the bark is raised.
4. Then slip the bud under the slit and trim off the excess.

35

Cutting the bud

When you cut the bud from the budstick, leave a shield below the bud to help hold the bud in place when it is inserted into the rootstock.

1. Hold the budstick by the top end with the lower end away from the body.
2. Place the knife 1/2 inch below the first suitable bud. With a shallow slicing movement, pass the knife beneath the bud approaching the surface 1 inch above it. The part around the bud will be the shield.

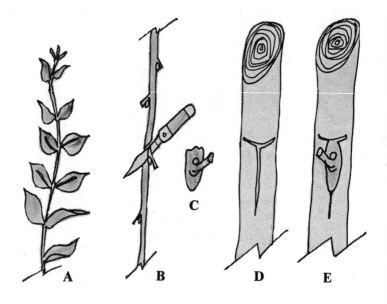

T-Budding

A *Source of buds*
B *Cutting the bud*
C *The shield bud*
D *T-cut in the stock*
E *Bud in place*
F *Bud tied in stock*
G *The branch cut off the stock*
   the following spring

36

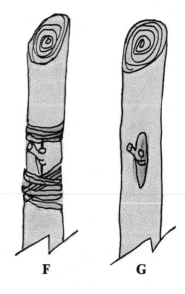

3. Cut the shield bearing the bud fairly thin, but not so thin that the soft growing tissue beneath the bark and wood is injured.
4. Retain the thin strip of wood that was cut with the shield.

Inserting the bud
1. After cutting, hold the bud by the petiole between the finger and thumb.
2. Insert the bud into the T-shape or the patch cut incision. Fast nurserymen that are experienced slip the bud on the knife directly into the cut. A properly inserted bud is at least 3/4 inch below the top transverse cut. Avoid undue manipulation or prying of the bark flaps.
3. Place the buds on the same side as the prevailing winds to prevent subsequent breakage.

Tying the bud
When the cambial layers are in close contact, they establish an intimate contact of the cambial region, usually producing thin-walled parenchyma cells that lead to interlocking cells, thus closing or briding the bud to the stock. Tying the bud to the rootstock will insure close contact.
1. After inserting the bud, wrap it snuggly. Rubber budding strips have largely replaced raffia or string. Rubber strips have the merit of expanding with growth of the rootstock. After exposure to the sun for a month or so, they will rot and fall off. By this time, a good union between bud and rootstock has taken place.
2. Be sure to leave the bud exposed.
3. Wrapping may be done either downward or upward. Pull the free end of the rubber strip under the last turn to hold it in place.

Caring after budding
The first indication you will have that the bud has united with the stock is that the leaf stem will drop off. In successful budding, the bud usually will have grown to the stock in 2 to 3 weeks. Shriveled adhering leaf stems often indicate failure. If the bark still separates readily from the wood, a new bud may be inserted in a new location on the stock.

Buds inserted in late July or later remain dormant until the following spring. Buds properly united with the stock do not require any winter protection such as banking soil around the budded stock. This eliminates two extra time-consuming operations, namely covering in the fall and uncovering in the spring. Cut off rootstock immediately above the grafted bud in early spring. Rub off all suckers that appear on the rootstock during the spring and early summer.

Grafting

To reproduce fruit or nut trees by grafting, the trunk of the seedling is cut off a few inches from the ground and material from .a known variety is joined to it by one of the grafting methods, such as whip-and-tongue graft or four-flap graft. This is normally done in late winter or early spring.

Whip-and-tongue graft

This type of propagating is done in the winter. The grafted stock is transplanted in rows in the spring.

1. Use 1-year-old wood that is smooth, straight and free from branches.
2. The diameters of the stock and scion should match.
3. From about 2 inches above the basal end of the scion, make a diagonal cut to the base.
4. Make the tongue by cutting straight about 1-1/4 inches half way along the cut surface. Make the cut toward the apical end of the scion.
5. Make similar cuts on the rootstock.
6. Interlock the scion and the rootstock so that the cambium layers make as much contact as possible.
7. Secure the graft union with rubber tape or waxed string and wrap the graft with foil and plastic.

Four-flap graft

This method has become increasingly popular. It can be used successfully on fruit or nut trees to change the variety or to get a pollinator limb on the tree.

The four-flap graft method allows the use of wood twice the diameter of that used in the whip-and-tongue graft. The four-flap's contact surface is much greater than others. The surface is entirely covered with the bark flaps to facilitate fast healing and a strong union. The four-flap graft does not require any close fits and, therefore, is a good graft for beginners. Although the graft works better if the scion and the stock are the same size, the graft can be made with wood 25% larger or smaller.

1. Collect the scion wood in February. Collect vigorous, mature, last year's growth.

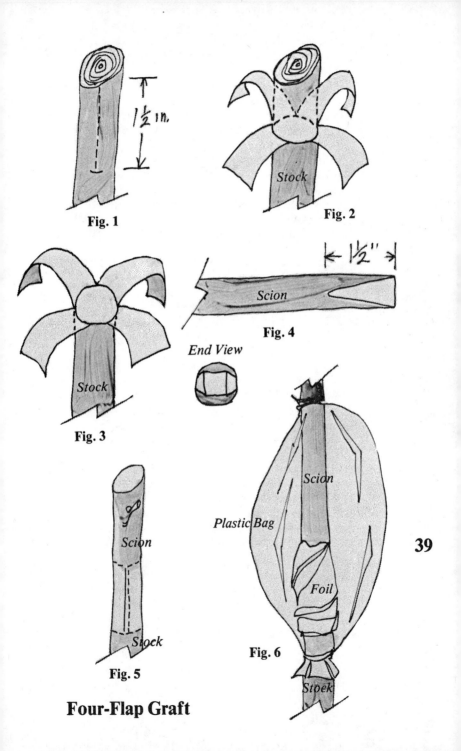

Fig. 1

Fig. 2

Fig. 3

Fig. 4

End View

Fig. 5

Fig. 6

39

Four-Flap Graft

2. Cut the wood into lengths of approximately 20 inches. Each length will make three grafts.

3. Dip the scion wood in water and sling out the excess.

4. Wrap in dry, new paper and plastic.

5. Store in a cool place (32°-35°F) such as a crisper in a refrigerator. Scion wood up to 1 inch in diameter can be used satisfactorily.

6. When you are ready to graft the scion wood to the rootstock, cut off the stock with a sharp knife or pruning shear at a point where the graft can be easily made. The stock should be about the same size as the scion.

7. Make 4 vertical cuts 1-1/2 inches long and equally spaced around the circumference of the stock. Make the cuts through the bark.

8. Pull back the bark forming 4 flaps. This will expose 1-1/2 inches of the stock.

9. Use sharp pruning shears to cut off the "plug." Be careful not to cut or damage the 4 flaps.

10. Use a sharp knife to cut the scion on 4 sides. Start the cut 1-1/2 inches from the end. Cut just under the bark. The end view will be square.

11. Insert the scion so that the 4 flaps will cover the 4 surfaces of the scion.

12. Wrap with plastic grafting tape or rubber tape. Leave the lower 1/4 inch of the graft exposed so that bleeding can drain out.

13. Cover the tape with aluminum foil. Then cover the entire graft with a plastic bag. Tie 1 inch below the foil.

14. After 3 or 4 weeks, growth should start. At this time, cut the plastic bag and pull it down to expose the scion.

15. Tie it 1 inch above the foil.

16. Three or four weeks later, remove the plastic, the plastic bag and foil and cut the tape.

17. Replace the foil to offer some protection for the graft. Tape again over the foil to keep the wind from blowing the graft out. The foil will compress a little to let the union grow.

18. Remove tape and foil in about a month. Remove the other growth on the stock when grafting and keep it in check during the growing season.

Fruits and Berries

Fruits and berries are grown, eaten and enjoyed in every country of the world. Although grapes have been grown since the earliest times, blackberries and strawberries have been cultivated only in the past 100 or 200 years. Even more recent are blueberries, which have been cultivated commercially for approximately 50 years. All are suited for growing on the country place, provided climate and soil conditions are suitable.

41

Fruits and berries make a valuable contribution to our diets. They are not only delicious in flavor, but also easily digested and stimulating to the appetite. The acids, salts and vitamins they contain are readily used by our bodies to maintain good health. They are an excellent source of vitamin C and valuable mineral salts, including iron, phosphorus and calcium. The water and roughage found in all fruits make them good natural laxatives. Experts on nutrition believe that a person's general health can be improved by adding more fruit to his or her diet.

Grapes

Grapes are probably one of the oldest cultivated plants in the world. They have been referred to in myths, in fables and in the Bible for as long as man has recorded history. Countless varieties are cultivated around the world. Depending upon the variety, they can be eaten fresh from the vine, dried into raisins, or made into grape juice, wine or jelly. In addition, the skins and seeds are used to make other products. The purple-colored ink used on meats by packers and govermnent inspectors is made from the skins of dark varieties of grapes. Grape seed oil is used to manufacture mayonnaise and potato chips, and to spray on raisins to keep them from sticking.

Grapes, an important commercial fruit, are extensively grown in home plantings. They are popular because they are easy to grow, bear early and regularly, and are small but long-lived plants. The increased interest in wine has stimulated grape growing both commercially and for home use. Excellent markets have developed for the sale of grapes to individuals who want to make their own wine.

Grapes are divided into four general groupings.

1. **Vinifera grapes** (European grapes). This grape first grew wild in southeastern Asia, but was later transplanted to Europe and grown there as the first cultivated grape. Early Spanish missionaries brought vinifera grape vines to America, but they did not grow well because it was too cold in the northern region and too humid in the southern regions. These grapes are very exacting in their requirements, and the areas where they can be grown are limited. Eventually, growers found that the vines thrived in California, so they started vineyards there. California has remained one of the most important grape-producing areas of the world. Most of the grapes raised commercially in the U.S., both for the fresh fruit market and for processing into wines, are grown there. The V. vinifera varieties are more susceptible to disease and insect damage than other varieties, and they do have exacting climatic requirements.

2. **American bunch grapes.** These grape varieties were derived primarily from wild grape species native to North America, which has been called a "natural vineyard." Although American bunch grapes make up only about 15 per cent of the total United States grape crop, they are grown over a far wider area than other types of grapes.

3. **Muscadine grapes.** These grapes are grown in the South Atlantic and Gulf Coast states. The muscadines are more resistant to diseases and insects in the hot, humid climate than other grape varieties. The muscadines differ from the other varieties in that the fruits grow in loose clusters instead of bunches.

4. **Hybrids.** Varieties have been developed in France over the past 80 years by crossing American bunch grape varieties with vinifera varieties. Selection has been based on their resistance to foliage diseases and the phylloxera root louse as well as their high production capability and suitability for wine. The varieties that have a high percentage of V. vinifera in their parentage usually have better quality fruit for table or wine use than varieties derived mainly from the American species. However, V. vinifera parentage

increases susceptibility to disease and insect damage. Therefore, a choice of a variety is usually a compromise between the fruit quality of V. vinifera and the ease of culture of the American species.

The hybrid varieties are generally referred to by the name or initials of the originator followed by his selection number. About 50 hybrids have been given names.

Planning and Preparation

Varieties

Grape varieties are available to suit most climatic conditions. Growing grapes is limited or entirely unsatisfactory in arid areas of the South or Southwest where irrigation is not possible. Production is also unsatisfactory in locations that have less than 150 days growing season, have extremely severe winter temperatures, or have high temperatures and extremely high humidity. The grapes are susceptible to several diseases which thrive under hot, humid conditions, so special varieties must be selected for such areas.

When you chose grape varieties for your area, consider the above information as well as the following factors.

1. **Minimum winter temperature.** Varieties differ in their ability to survive low temperatures.

2. **Growing season.** Varieties also differ in the number of frost-free days required for the fruit to develop and ripen. Time of ripening is a general indication of where a variety can be grown successfully. Midseason varieties ripen about the same time as Concord, a standard in the grape growing industry, and have a wide area of adaptation. The Concord requires at least 170 days of frost-free weather to reach proper maturity. The early ripening varieties ripen 2 to 4 weeks before Concord and are grown in areas having a shorter season. Late season varieties are best adapted to the South where there is a long, warm growing season.

3. **Irrigation water.** Even in areas of high rainfall, a system to irrigate the vineyard during dry conditions will insure a high quality fruit.

4. **Vineyard site.** Because you probably have limited acreage and not much flexibility in site selection, pay more attention to varieties that will produce on your site.

5. **Disease and insect resistance.** If you have knowledge of existing diseases, select varieties that are resistant rather than trying to combat the disease.

6. **Economics.** Be sure that a market exists for the variety you select. The best bet is to select a proven variety that is grown in your area. For home use, select a wider variety. Even though some

of your choices may produce well in some years and little or none in other years, they probably will provide enough fruit to justify maintaining the vines.

Site location

If you have a choice, select a site on well-drained soil in a relatively frost-free area. The best site is on level or gently sloping land that is somewhat elevated. Steep slopes are subject to erosion and make spraying difficult during wet periods when disease control is of the utmost importance. Rows should be straight except on steep slopes where they should be contoured.

Planting

Preparing to plant

Prepare the site by plowing and disking. If the site is in sod or has not been cultivated for some time, grow a row crop for at least one season before preparing the land for grapes.

Planting the vines

In the South, plant vines as soon as they are dormant in the fall. Fall planting allows the vines to start growth as soon as the weather permits, even though the soil may not be in condition to work.

In colder areas, fall-planted vines must be mounded with earth to protect against frost heaving and winter damage. Because of this, extra work and possible loss of vines may occur. Early spring planting is generally preferred north of Arkansas, Tennessee and Virginia. In spring, plant grapevines as soon as the soil can be worked so that they will be well established by the time the hot, dry summer weather arrives.

46

Set the strongest 1-year-old vines available. Two-year-old vines are seldom worth the extra cost. They will not bear fruit any sooner than well grown 1-year-old plants. Plant grapevines about the same depth they grew in the nursery, and prune them to a single stem 2 or 3 buds long. Most varieties should be spaced 8 to 10 feet apart in the row with the rows 10 to 12 feet apart.

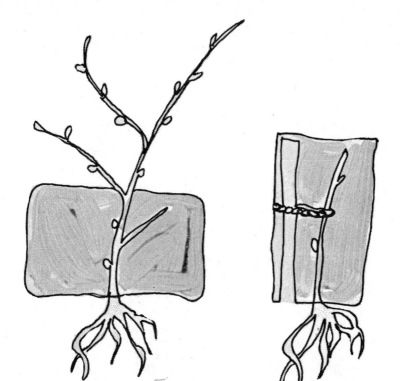

NEWLY PLANTED GRAPEVINE
BEFORE PRUNING

AFTER PRUNING

Soil Management

Cultivation

Cultivate the vineyard by plowing shallowly 3 to 4 inches deep **47**
in the spring. Then disk or harrow the soil throughout the summer
to control weeds and grass. Use a grape hoe or rotor tiller in the
rows under the vines to control weeds and grass. Hand hoeing
should be used if necessary. Herbicides have been developed for
specific use in vineyards. If you use a herbicide follow the manu-
facturer's directions.

Fertilizers

Cultivation and fertilizers will stimulate weak vines to make
them vigorous and more productive. Lack of vigor in a vineyard is

normally from poor care. Spring is the best time to fertilize. Grapes respond to nitrogen fertilizer more than other minerals. However, fertilize only after a soil test is done to determine the kind and amount of fertilizer the soil requires.

Cover crops

Cover crops, such as vetch, blue lupine, clover, rye, wheat or oats, should be grown and turned under to increase the organic matter in the vineyard. Drill the seed instead of broadcasting.

Training and Pruning

The training and pruning are interdependent operations. Young vines are trained to a system of growth on the trellis or other support by pruning. The mature vines are pruned to maintain the system of growth and to insure the production of good quality fruit.

The American bunch grapes are normally raised on a trellis system consisting of wire strung between posts. Set the plants directly under the trellis. If the plants are out of line, they may be constantly injured during cultivation. Do not set vines against treated wood posts, but set 2 or 3 vines between the posts. If you use steel or concrete posts, set the plants next to the posts and at midpoints.

Muscadines are also grown using the trellis system. They should be spaced farther apart in the row depending on the variety. Do not prune back muscadines as much as other grapes.

The vinifera grapes are sometimes pruned and trained to grow on a post cross-piece system. This enables cultivation in both directions.

48

Making a trellis

1. Construct a trellis system of 2 or more No. 9 gauge wires attached to posts set 20 to 24 feet apart.
2. Set the end posts at least 3 feet deep and brace them properly.
3. Set the line posts 2 feet deep.
4. Staple the wires on the windward side of the posts. Be sure the staples are loose enough so the wire can slide back and forth to facilitate tightening.
5. Tighten the wires each spring before the vines are tied.

6. Ground each wire in the trellis. Set a few steel posts to permit proper grounding. An ungrounded trellis can be damaged due to lightning.
7. Leave enough room at the end of the trellis so that equipment can be turned.

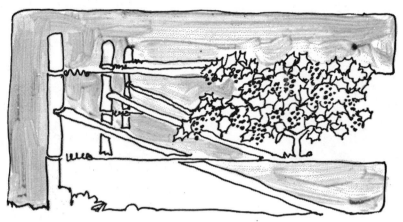

TRELLIS SYSTEM

Training systems

There are several good training systems. Some are better for one variety than another. You can get good results using one of the two following systems.

1. **The four-arm Kniffin system.** This is the most popular system for bunch grapes. It gives good production, requires little **49** summer tying, and is adapted to most varieties.

The trellis consists of two wires. After the first growing season and during the dormant period, select the most vigorous cane for the trunk and tie it to the top wire. Cut the cane off above the wire and remove all other canes. If no cane is long enough to reach the top wire, tie the strongest to the bottom wire and extend it to the top wire the next season.

After the second year, select 4 vigorous canes for the arms. Prune the canes to approximately 10 buds in length, depending on variety, and lay them down along the wires and tie them. Cut 4

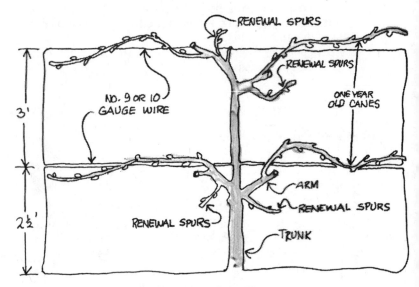

FOUR-ARM KNIFFIN SYSTEM

other canes back to 2 or 3 buds in length for renewal spurs. Remove all other canes. Each winter thereafter, replace the arms with the canes from the renewal spurs, and leave new renewal spurs.

2. **The Munson system.** This system is used in home plantings. It is particularly suitable for humid climates because the fruit is produced high above the ground where it is less subject to injury by disease. The Munson system is also suited to very vigorous varieties and to Muscadine grapes.

The trellis consists of 3 wires strung in the shape of a wide V. Two wires are attached to the outer edges of cross arms 24 to 30 inches wide and 5 feet above the ground. The third wire is attached to the post 6 or 8 inches lower.

Train the vine to a single trunk extending to the lower wire. After the second growing season (during the dormant period), prune to 2 or more canes and 2 renewal spurs. Tie the arms along the lower wire. As the shoots develop during the next growing season, distribute them over the upper wires, allowing the shoots to hang down. Each winter replace the arms with canes from renewal spurs and leave new renewal spurs.

If a system that differs greatly from one of the two described here is used in your area, check with a local grower to determine how the system functions and construction details. There is probably a special reason for the system being used in that area.

Pruning

Grapevines must be pruned heavily annually. Proper pruning is essential for consistent yields and good quality fruit. Pruning prevents overproduction of fruit by limiting the number of buds. Underpruned vines become weak and produce small clusters of fruit. If vines are overpruned, however, they become excessively vegetative. The lack of proper pruning has caused more failures in grape production than any other cause.

Grapevines should be pruned during the dormant season. This is usually during the winter or spring. Where winter weather is mild, prune anytime during the dormant season as long as the temperature is not below freezing. Frozen canes become brittle and are easy to break. Pruning prior to hard freezes can cause winter damage. If you prune late in the spring, you might have difficulty tying the vines without destroying many of the buds. Vines pruned in the spring will "bleed", but this really does not hurt the vines. Late pruning may cause delay in the plants leafing out.

The vigor of a mature vine indicates how much fruit it can produce. The more vigorous the vine, the more buds should be left after pruning. Varieties for which long-cane pruning is recommended, such as Concord and Muscadine, should have between 30 and 60 buds after pruning. The rule of thumb is to leave the basic 30 buds (unless the vine is very weak), plus 10 buds for each pound of 1-year-old wood that is removed. Varieties for which medium-cane pruning is recommended should have 25 buds, plus 10 buds for each pound of wood removed, up to a maximum of 45 buds.

Large cluster varieties should be pruned much more severely than Concord. The hybrid varieties for which short-cane pruning is recommended should be cut back to as few as 4 to 6 buds for the first pound of wood removed, plus 2 buds for each additional pound removed. After practice, you will be able to prune without weighing the wood; however, it is still a good idea to weigh the prunings of a few vines to check for accuracy.

No system is completely satisfactory for all areas. If the common practice is different in your area, check with local growers as to the reasons. Some varieties will react differently under different climates or soil conditions.

Pruning after a late frost

A late frost or freeze may damage the new spring growth of grapes. If this happens, remove all new growth of injured and uninjured parts. Grapes have multiple buds, and when the first bud is removed, a secondary bud will normally develop to take the re-removed bud's place. The secondary bud will develop and make a partial crop. The vines need to be stripped completely to force the secondary buds to develop.

Tie the cane to the trellis before the buds start to swell because the buds are easily rubbed or knocked off. Use binder twine or some material that will retain its strength for several months. Wire or plastic may last too long and girdle the vine. Use a knot that will not slip (bowline), tie the arm tightly at the end just behind the last bud, and pinch the bud off. The other ties should be loose to allow for growth of the vine.

Harvesting

The harvest date of grapes varies depending upon how the grapes will be used. The harvest time for grapes used in wine and juice is determined by the percentage of soluble solids or sugar content. The testing is done with a refractometer or a balling hydrometer. Table grapes are usually harvested by taste or by the color of the seeds, which change from green to brown as the grapes mature.

Color is usually a poor index of maturity. Many varieties change color long before they are ripe. Practically all grapes become sweeter and less acid as they mature. Sometimes it is necessary to harvest grapes a little before they are fully ripe to prevent losses or for shipment to markets.

Birds sometimes do damage to ripe grapes. In home plantings, clusters on just a few vines can be protected by bagging them with kraft paper bags or by covering the vines with netting.

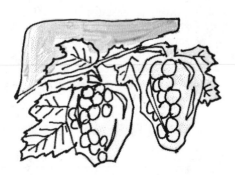

A well-managed vineyard should produce from 4 to 6 tons of grapes per acre. Yields from some of the more successful growers in favorable locations produce up to 12 tons per acre.

Insects and Diseases

Good yields and high quality fruit cannot be expected unless a good spray program is followed to control insects and diseases. Unsprayed vines in home gardens sometimes produce fine clusters, but the odds are against it.

Grape phylloxera

This small plant louse, or aphid, is the most destructive grape pest found in the western United States and Europe. It sucks the sap from the leaves and roots causing small galls about the size of the head of a match. The galls on the underside of the grape leaves are open and contain several small, wingless, yellowish aphids. The aphids also cause the roots to rot and the foliage to turn yellow, which results in a general decrease in vigor. Usually the vines will die within 3 to 10 years after root infestation.

The grape phylloxera is native to the eastern United States. The vines in that section of the country have acquired practical immunity to them; however, they do considerable damage in the western part of the United States and in Europe. The best method of control has been to graft canes of the desired variety onto resistant rootstock from immune vines. Almost all grapes sold in nurseries are grafted onto native rootstocks, but be sure to check before purchasing the vines.

Grape flea beetle

The grape flea bettle is a small jumping beetle, usually about 1/5 inch long, with a dark metallic greenish-blue color. It eats the buds off the vine just as they start to unfold in the spring. You can tell the grape flea beetle is around because the newly opening foliage looks ragged and tattered. Light brown, black-spotted grubs about 1/3 inch long will usually be found along with the beetles feeding on the newly opening leaves.

53

The grape flea beetle is found in the eastern two-thirds of the United States. The beetles can be controlled by insecticides if they are used as soon as the beetles make their appearance on the vines in the spring. On a few backyard vines, the insect may be controlled by spreading a piece or cloth, dipped in oil, under the vines and jarring the beetles onto it. Fall cleanup of the grape vines will also help to keep down the numbers of this insect.

Grape berry moth

The grape berry moth is almost universally present wherever

grapes are grown — whether in the largest vineyards or on the smallest backyard grapevine. The grape berries become webbed together, turn a dark purple and drop from the stems when the grapes are about the size of a pea. Small holes are eaten in the nearly ripened grapes, the sides of which are attached by a light web to a portion of the leaf or to adjoining berries. Small silken cocoons appear in semicircular flaps cut in the grape leaves, which are folded over and held together by a light web. When this insect is abundant, it can destroy up to 90 percent of the grapes in an unsprayed vineyard.

This insect is troublesome in the northeastern fourth of the United States and in southeastern Canada and extends westward to Wisconsin and Nebraska and southward to Alabama and Louisiana. This insect can be controlled with an insecticide applied with a high pressure sprayer. In addition to following a spraying program, rake up and burn the fallen leaves during the fall or winter, or plow the vineyard and adjacent areas as soon as the ground becomes frost-free in the spring.

Grape leafhopper

The grape leafhopper is a small, pale yellowish, red-flecked, very active insect that sucks the sap from the undersides of the grape leaves. Very small whitish spots appear over the grape leaves, which later become dry and shriveled. The entire leaf becomes a pale greenish-yellow, the vines show poor vigor, and the foliage appears sickly.

The leafhopper is universally present, year in and year out, becoming active about the time the leaves are half grown. It can be controlled by pre- and post-bloom spraying. Because adult leafhoppers, like most of the other grape insects, spend the winter in shelters provided by trash, weeds or grasses, a thorough cleanup of the vineyard is of much value in helping to control this pest.

Grape rootworm

The grape rootworm changes from a small, brown-headed grub measuring up to 1/2 inch long into a small brown or grayish-tan beetle about 1/4 inch long that emerges about 2 weeks after the grapes bloom. As a small whitish grub, it eats off the small feeder roots and gouges out channels in the bark of the larger roots. The beetles feed upon the leaves throughout the summer making a series of small holes in chain-like rows. This causes the leaves to turn yellow and the vines to become weak so that little new growth occurs.

The grape rootworm is found in the eastern part of the United States, except in the extreme north and south. The beetles may be controlled by thoroughly spraying with an insecticide as soon as the feeding punctures on the leaves are noticed. Intensive shallow cultivation of the soil, up to the time of the emergence of the adults in late June, will destroy many of the pupae.

Fungi
Four fungi destroy grapes: powdery mildew, downy mildew, black rot and anthracnose. They can be controlled by the use of dusts and sprays.

Study the diseases and insects that appear to be prevalent in your particular area, and use recommended sprays or dusts to control them. Most areas will require spraying at least three times a year, with more required during wet seasons. For information on insects and diseases and the best methods of control, consult with your local county agent.

One parting word of wisdom; grapes are like children, they need a lot of love and attention.

Varieties
Obtain planting stocks from a nursery that specializes in grapes, if at all possible. However, most nurseries carry a few of the more popular varieties. Be sure that the varieties you select have been grafted onto phylloxera-resistant rootstocks native to the eastern United States. In the following information the symbol (B) means blue or purple, the symbol (R) means red, and the symbol (W) means white or greenish.

Beta
(B) Ripens very early. Vigorous, productive, very hardy. Small clusters and berries with high sugar and high acid; wild taste. Used mostly for jellies, jams, and juice. Prune to long canes. Adapted to northern United States and high elevations.

Blue Lake
(R) Recommended for the Gulf Coast area and Florida area where it ripens early midseason. Medium clusters of small grapes. Spicy flavor suitable for juice and jelly; does not ship or store well. Prune to medium cane.

Caco
(R) Ripens Midseason. Very vigorous, moderately productive, hardy. Suitable for table use and roadside market. The berries are large, but not too good quality. Prune to long canes.

Campbell Early

(B) Ripens early midseason. Moderately vigorous, moderately productive, fairly hardy. Clusters medium to large; sometimes has poor sets; berries medium. Used commercially for juice in the Northwest. Prune to long cane.

Catawba

(R-B) Ripens late midseason. Vigorous, productive, nardy. Large clusters and berries. Grown commercially for wine, but suitable for juice and table use. Prune to medium cane.

Concord

(B) Ripens midseason. Vigorous, productive, hardy, disease resistant. Medium clusters of medium to large berries; the standard of the industry. Leading commercial variety, used primarily for juice, jelly and special wines. Prune to long cane.

Concord Seedless

(B) Ripens midseason. Low vigor, moderately productive, hardy, disease resistant. Small clusters of small, almost seedless berries with typical Concord flavor. For table use or for grape pie. Prune to medium cane.

Delaware

(R) Ripens late midseason. Medium to low vigor, fairly productive, hardy. Medium-small clusters of small berries, which are often picked when still pink. Will ripen to mahogany color with high sugar content. Standard of quality for table use. Prune to medium long canes.

Ellen Scott

(R) Ripens late. Vigorous, productive, only moderately hardy, susceptible to disease. Medium-large clusters of large berries. A juice and table grape for the warmer areas. Prune to medium cane.

56

Fredonia

(B) Ripens early midseason. Vigorous, productive, hardy, disease resistant. Medium to small clusters of large berries. Flavor similar to Concord, but milder. Recommended for roadside markets. Prune to long canes.

Golden Muscat

(W) Ripens late midseason. Vigorous, moderately productive, moderately hardy. Large clusters of medium-sized berries with a foxy-muscat flavor. Table variety. Quality of fruit suffers in hot weather. Prune to medium cane.

Himrod
(W) Ripens early midseason. Vigorous, productive, only medium hardy, requires careful spraying. Large loose clusters of medium-sized berries, oval, nearly seedless. Table variety. Very popular for roadside stands. Prune to medium canes.

Interlaken Seedless
(W) Ripens early. Moderately vigorous and productive, somewhat tender to cold. Requires careful spraying. Medium clusters of small nearly seedless berries. Table variety. Popular roadside market grape. Prune to medium cane.

Joannes-Seyve 23-416
(W-R) Late midseason ripening. Very vigorous, moderate production, good disease resistance. Large, loose clusters of oval, pinkish berries. Wine quality good in southern Concord area. Prune to medium cane.

Joannes-Seyve 26-205
(B) Also known as *Chambourcin.* Late midseason. Moderate vigor, productive, disease resistant. Large clusters. Wine good in southern Concord area. Prune to short cane.

Kuhlmann 188-2
(B) Also known as *Fock.* Very early. Moderate vigor and production, small, tight clusters of small berries, fair disease resistance. Very good wine in the cooler areas. Prune to long cane.

Landot 244
(B) Also known as *Landel.* Midseason. Moderate to good vigor, moderate production, fair disease resistance. Medium-sized cluster. Wine quality very good when fruit is fully ripe. Prune to medium cane.

Moore Early
(B) Early midseason. Moderate vigor and low production, hardy. Medium cluster with large berries. Cracks badly. Prune to medium canes.

Niagara
(W) Midseason. Vigorous, productive, hardy, disease resistant. Medium-sized compact cluster of large berries. Flavor foxy. Suitable for table use. Prune to long cane.

Ravat 51
(W) Also known as *Vignoles.* Early midseason. Vigorous, moderately productive, very hardy, requires careful spraying. Clusters small, very compact, and subject to ripe rots. Wine quality very good in cool areas. Prune to long canes.

Seibel 4986

(W) Also known as *Rayon d'Or*. Late midseason. Moderately vigorous, somewhat cold tender; consistent, though moderate. Medium to large clusters; medium-sized berries are pink at maturity. Good resistance to foliage diseases, but subject to fruit rot. Wine quality fair in northern areas to very good in central areas. Slightly foxy in hot, dry seasons. Prune to short canes.

Seibel 5279

(W) Also known as *Aurore*. Early. Vigorous, productive, hardy, moderate disease resistance. Medium-long, loose clusters. Good quality wine when grown in cool area. Prune to medium canes.

Seibel 7053

(B) Also known as *Chancellor*. Late midseason. Vigorous and productive; must be sprayed carefully. Clusters medium and slightly loose; berries medium. Wine bland when grown in southern area. Prune to short canes.

Seibel 9549

(W) Also known as *Verdelet*. Midseason. Vigorous, variable production, somewhat cold tender, requires careful spraying. Large, loose clusters of oval berries which are excellent for table use. Wine fair to good. Prune to short canes for best clusters.

Seibel 13053

(B) Also known as *Cascade*. Very early. Hardy, moderately productive, moderately disease resistant. Clusters medium to small with medium berries. Fruit color pale unless left until fully ripe. Especially subject to bird damage. Prune to medium canes.

Seneca

(W) Early. Moderately vigorous, productive, moderately hardy, susceptible to powdery mildew, resistant to fruit rot. Medium-sized clusters with oval, crisp berries of excellent table quality. An outstanding variety with proper disease control. Prune to medium canes.

58

Seyve-Villard 5-276

(W) Also known as *Seyval Blanc*. Early midseason. Moderately vigorous, productive. Large clusters, good foliage, disease resistant, but subject to fruit rot. Makes very good wine. Prune to short canes.

S.V. 12-375

(W) Also known as *Villard Blanc*. Late. Very vigorous, highly productive, highly disease resistant. Clusters medium to large. Acceptable for table use. Wine good. Prune to short canes.

S.V. 18-315

(B) Also known as *Villard Moies*. Late. Vigorous in warmer areas, productive, disease resistant. Medium to large clusters. Wine very good. Prune to short canes.

Steuben

(B) Late midseason. Vigorous, productive, medium hardy, disease resistant. Moderately large clusters of medium berries. Pleasant spicy-muscat flavor. Excellent for table use. If slightly overcropped, fruit remains red and vine is subject to cold damage. Prune to medium canes.

Stover

(W) Recommended only for the Gulf Coast-Florida area, where it is early, moderately vigorous, productive and hardy. Resistant to Pierce's Disease, but must be sprayed for foliage diseases. Medium clusters of medium size; oval berries which hold in storage; table variety. Prune to medium canes.

Vidal 256

(W) Late. Very vigorous, productive, fair disease resistance. Handsome long clusters with small berries. Can produce a fair crop if frost destroys primary crop. Wine quality good to very good. Prune to medium canes.

Worden

(B) Early midseason. Vigorous, productive, hardy. Medium to large clusters of large Concord-type berries. Subject to fruit cracking. Prune to long canes.

Strawberries

The strawberry, a small plant belonging to the rose family, has been cultivated in the United States for almost 150 years. It is considered one of the most important fruits grown in the Western Hemisphere. The plant was originally known as the "strewberry," probably because the berries seem to be strewn or scattered among the leaves of the plant. In time, however, it gradually came to be called "strawberry."

Americans are particularly fond of strawberries. Although they are grown in every state in the Union, until recently strawberries could be purchased only during a relatively short period of time in the spring. Now, however, because of an expanded growing area and the adaptability of the strawberry to quick freezing, they can be enjoyed year around either fresh or frozen. In addition to being eaten fresh sprinkled with sugar or covered with milk or cream, they are also used to make jelly and preserves, pastries, ice cream and desserts, the most notable being strawberry shortcake.

You can benefit several ways from raising strawberries. They make an excellent contribution to the family diet. They can be used to open the roadside market a few weeks earlier in the spring while other fruits and vegetables are becoming mature enough for marketing. Also, strawberries can be raised commercially on small acreage provided the soil and climate are suitable and water is available for irrigation. In almost all areas, strawberries require some irrigation if they are to be raised profitably.

Planning and Preparation

Location

Factors that determine a favorable strawberry-growing location are the ripening time of the fruit, transportation facilities and available pickers. Fruit grown in the South is usually marketed when there is little competition from other regions, and, thus, enjoys a price advantage. Shipments start in December and January in southern Florida, and in February and March from central and northern Florida. In the latter part of April, shipments from the Carolinas become heavy, and by May and June, the areas farther north become the prime suppliers. There are similar successions of strawberry shipments on the West Coast and in Louisiana, Alabama, Mississippi, Texas and other states up the Mississippi Valley.

Varieties

Hundreds of varieties of strawberries are grown in the United States. Most, however, are for local use and are not suitable for shipment over long distances. If you plan to sell your berries on the local market, use a variety that is being grown locally. If you plan to ship strawberries to distant markets, consider one or more of the following leading varieties: Headliner, Dabreak, Blakemore, Albritton, Florida Ninety, Earlibelle and Pocohontas. Consult the county agent and local growers before making a variety selection.

Soil and cover crops

Strawberries grow in a wide range of soils, from sand to heavy gumbo. The soil must have good drainage; strawberries are seriously injured when subjected to standing water. Leaf, root and fruit diseases are more frequent on poorly drained soils. Humus in the soil is very important for strawberries. It can be added by applying manure or by growing and turning under one or more green manure crops before planting the field to strawberries. Legumes, such as clover, cowpeas, crotalaria and soybeans, are preferred as green manure crops. The soil should be thoroughly tilled and then bedded into ridges 6 to 9 inches high. The width will vary from 3 to 6 feet, depending on the planting system used.

Temperature

Daylight periods of 12 hours or less and cool temperatures are very important in flowerbud formation. Because different varieties have different daylight and temperature requirements, you need to pick a variety adapted to your local area.

After the flowerbuds form, the plants become dormant, except in the Deep South. As the weather warms in the spring, the flowerbuds develop. If freezing weather occurs at this point, the flower clusters may be killed. However, the warm weather that causes flower clusters to grow also enables the plants to develop more flowerbuds to replace those that are killed. The first flower to open on a cluster is the largest; the first flower develops into the largest berry. The next flower develops into the second largest berry, and so on.

Planting

The strawberry plant grows a little differently from most other plants, including other berries. Healthy strawberry plants set out in a moist soil produce new, fibrous roots within a few days. New leaves appear almost as soon as the new roots. If the new root system is extensive, the new leaves will be large and healthy.

Planting systems

Two planting systems are generally used in commercial operations:

1. **The Hill System.** The plants are set out in late summer or early autumn, and the crop is harvested in late winter or early spring. Usually, plants set at that time do not produce any runners; if they do appear, they should be pruned off. One or two rows can be planted on the bed in the hill system. Most growers use a mulch of black polyethylene plastic on the rows. Place the plastic over the bed and set the plants in holes punched in the plastic. Or you can set the plants out first and pull them through holes in the plastic. Most of the commercial acreages planted in Florida, California and Louisiana are planted in this manner.

2. **The Matted-Row System.** Plants are usually set in the early spring, spaced 18 to 40 inches apart in rows 3-1/2 to 4 feet apart. Runners will appear from buds in the leaf axils in 30 to 75 days and will continue to appear until autumn or a little later. Allow the runners to root and train them to form a solid mat in the spaces between plants. When the days shorten to about 12 hours in the fall, the growing points in the crowns of the oldest and largest plants start changing into flowerbuds. The beds are then mulched with hay or straw to protect them during the dormant period. The berries are harvested the next year after setting out the plants.

Planting the berries

When you obtain plants for the fields, buy plants that have been raised by a reliable nursery and are free from nematodes. Anthracnose disease organism does not live-over in the soil, so the best control is to use nursery plants known to be free of that disease.

After you get the plants from the nursery, keep them cool and moist until they are set. If they cannot be set for several days, open the packages, separate the plants, and "heel" them in, or place the entire package in cold storage at 32° to 40° F.

63

HEELING-IN STRAWBERRY PLANTS

Consider the following points when you set the plants. Most farmers set the plants by hand.

1. Set the plant so the crown is even with the surface of the ground after the soil has been packed firmly around the roots. Plants that are set too deep will smother; those that are set too shallow will dry out.
2. The soil must be firmly packed around the roots. If the soil is not properly firmed, air gets to the roots and dries them out. If the soil is dry, you will need to water the plants as they are set.
3. When setting the plants, it is easier if two people work together. One person inserts a spade or trowel into the ground, forcing an opening about 6 inches deep, and presses forward to open the slot in the soil. The second person carries the plants and inserts them in the slots. After the roots are inserted, the first person withdraws the spade and presses the soil firmly about the roots with the foot.

Flower stems will start forming soon after the plants are set out. Cut off these stems because they are a severe drain on the plants' vitality. This will also promote early runner plants, which will produce the most fruit the following year.

STRAWBERRY PLANT

STRAWBERRY BLOSSOM

64

Life of a plant

The length of time a planting remains profitable depends on the fertility of the soil, diseases, insects, weeds and management. If plants become diseased or heavily infested with weeds, destroy the planting and make a new planting on other fields. Plant the old field in a green manure crop for a couple of years before resetting it in strawberries.

Growers seldom renew strawberries that are planted in the hill system. They are normally plowed under at the end of the harvest season.

If you want to renew a planting, cut the tops of the plants off with a mowing machine and turn or rototill the mulch into the soil. This will improve the texture of the soil. The plants may be thinned by running a spike-toothed harrow or cultivator across the rows. Under favorable conditions, the plants will develop new foliage within 2 or 3 weeks, and the field will have the appearance of a new planting.

Soil Management

Irrigation

Some type of irrigation is almost a must for successful strawberry operations. Even a small drought during the growing season can cause serious losses. The berries must have abundant moisture during the final development stage. More growers use the sprinkler system than any other system. However, most irrigation systems can be made to work satisfactorily on strawberries.

Cultivation

If black plastic mulch is applied with the Hill System, you will not need to cultivate, to control weeds. However, you may need to run the middles with a plow. In fields where the plastic is not used, cultivate immediately after planting and continue throughout the growing season to control weeds. You may need to hoe the weeds from around the young plants. New roots from the crown grow out at the base of the new leaves. Because dry air kills these new roots, hoe and cultivate moist soil toward the plants to give the new roots a chance to form.

Mulching

Mulching the strawberries with hay, straw, or pine needles is still practiced by some growers. The principal reasons for mulching are to keep the berries clean, to prevent decay, to conserve moisture, to protect the flowers from frost and to keep down weeds. The mulch should be 1 to 3 inches deep after it has settled. Injury from late frost can be prevented by using mulch and a light spray irrigation. In cool weather, the flower can be pollinated over a period of several days so that the plants can be left covered with mulch for

2 or 3 days, if frost is expected. At the end of this time, pull the mulch back so that bees can get to the flowers for pollination.

Fertilizing
Fertilizer is required on most soils to grow a profitable crop of strawberries. Because of the wide variety of soils used in strawberry production, it is not possible to recommend the kind or amount to use. The soil should be tested and fertilizer applied in accordance with the results of such tests. Strawberries normally require per acre from 1000 to 2000 pounds of a commercial fertilizer such as 5-10-5. Broadcast part of this amount into the soil before planting. Apply the rest when the plants are to be set. Nitrogen fertilizer is sometimes side dressed next to the young plant in late summer or fall.

Acidity
Strawberries usually grow well on light soils where the acidity measures pH 5.5 to 6.5. They may grow well where the acidity measures pH 5.0 to 7.0 if there is a great amount of organic matter in the soil. Lime is needed if the pH is below 5.3. Lime will also "tie up" free aluminum that may be in the soil, which is toxic to strawberries. It will also make calcium and magnesium available to the strawberry plants. It is best to lime the soil a year or two before planting strawberries.

Pollination
The flowers on strawberry plants are pollinated mainly by honeybees. The flowering season will vary, but normally it will be

BEE POLLINATING
FLOWER

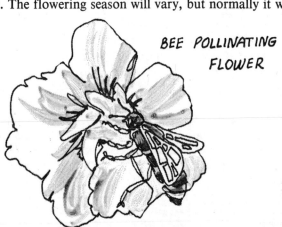

from 4 to 6 weeks — longer with cool weather and shorter with warm weather. The berries will also mature faster as the weather becomes warmer.

Harvesting

When harvesting strawberries, great care must be taken if the berries are to reach the market in the best condition. Pick the berries at least every other day. At the height of the season, they may require picking every day. Do not leave ripe berries in the field, because at the next picking, they will be too soft. One soft berry in a basket may spoil the entire basket. Pinch off the stem of each berry when it is picked, and leave about a half inch of stem attached to the berry. Place the berries gently in the basket. Do not pour berries or drop them, and do not leave them in the sun.

Insects and Diseases

The most widely destructive insects affecting strawberries are the strawberry flea beetle, strawberry root aphid, strawberry rootworms, strawberry weevils and white grubs.

The strawberry flea beetle

This beetle is very small, is metallic blue in color and measures less than 1/6 inch across. The beetles feed on the strawberry plants early in the spring and damage the plants before they start to bloom. The leaves become riddled with large numbers of small round holes and often dry up and turn brown. These beetles are found throughout the United States, and can usually be controlled by a thorough application of methoxychlor about one week before the strawberries bloom.

Strawberry root aphid

This aphid usually passes the winter in the form of shiny black eggs attached to the leaves and stems of the plants. The eggs hatch early in the spring into dark bluish-green aphids which feed on the new leaves of the strawberry plant. When these aphids become abundant, they are soon found by colonies of brown cornfield ants, who carry them to the plant's roots where they feed by sucking the sap from the roots. Infestation by these aphids causes the plants to lack vigor, the foliage to be pale in color, and the fruit to dry up or fail to mature properly. These aphids are found east of the Rocky Mountains. You can control root infestation by making certain that you select uninfested plants to start new beds. Also cultivate the ground deeply and thoroughly in early spring to break up and destroy the ants which may be present in the soil. The leaf-infesting forms may be controlled by spraying. Ask your nursery man which spray to use.

Strawberry rootworms

Strawberry rootworms are white, brown-spotted grubs about 1/8 inch long that pass the winter as copper-colored beetles. The grubs come out of their winter shelters in early spring and feed on the roots of the plants during May, June and July. The grubs turn into beetles during August, and as beetles destroy the foliage of the plants during early fall. This insect is found over most of the United States. It can normally be controlled by spraying or dusting the plants as the beetles leave hibernation, usually about the time the blossoms appear. July plowing of infested areas will destroy the larvae. Rotation of beds is also a good idea.

Strawberry weevil

The strawberry weevil passes the winter as a dark reddish-brown snout beetle measuring 1/12 to 1/8 inch long, usually sheltered under trash. The adults become active early in the spring about the time the strawberries start to bloom. The beetles puncture the buds with their long snouts and lay their eggs, which hatch into white legless, soft-bodied grubs. They kill the buds and fruits and leave them hanging on partially severed stems. This insect is found in the eastern United States and can be controlled by dusting or spraying the foliage as needed. Clean cultivation and planting resistant varieties help in control, as will planting one row of staminate variety to each five rows of pistillate varieties.

White grubs

This insect is a common enemy of the strawberry. Large white grubs with brown heads feed on the roots of the plants causing the plants to die. Once infested, it is almost impossible to rid a bed without plowing it up. In planting new beds, select an area that has been in some clean cultivated crop for one or two years because the June beetles prefer to lay their eggs in grassy or weedy areas. If possible, locate the beds some distance from the trees on which the beetles feed and near which they usually deposit their eggs. Thorough cultivation of the soil in the spring before the strawberries are set out will provide some benefit, but will not clean all the grubs out of the soil. Application of one handful (about 1.5 ounces) of a 1-20 mixture of lead arsenate and sand to the hole when the plants are set out will control the grubs. Another method of control is to spray or dust the soil with a suitable insecticide that is then harrowed into the soil to a depth of 4 to 6 inches.

Other diseases

Several diseases attack strawberries at all stages of development, including fruit rot; leaf, root and crown diseases; viruses and nematodes. Some diseases can be controlled by careful selection of planting stock and others by spraying with fungicides. Certain diseases, however, cannot be controlled once they infest a bed. Because many of the diseases are local in nature, you should become familiar with the insects and diseases prevalent in your area. Contact the local county agent for the best methods of controlling them.

Blackberries

The blackberry plant, a member of the rose family, grows clusters of cylindrical-shaped berries on slender stems that are attached to the main stalk of the plant. Although the blackberry grows wild in many areas of the country, it has been cultivated since the 1800's. Blackberries make an excellent contribution to the family diet. They can be used to make jams, jellies, preserves and wine, or can be eaten as fresh fruit topped with milk or cream. They also make delicious pies and blackberry cobbler.

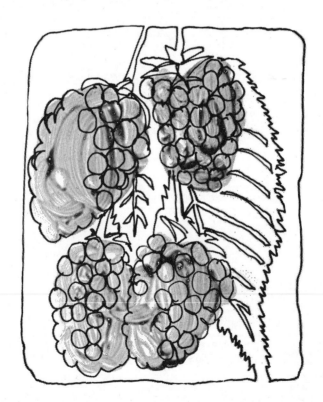

Blackberries grow best in temperate climates. They are not adapted to the mountain states, the desert southwest or the plains area, where the summers are hot and dry and the winters are severe. Hot, dry summers are hard on blackberry vines even after the berries are harvested. Dry weather during the berry season greatly reduces the yield and quality of the berries.

Planning and Preparation

Varieties

There are two basic types of blackberries — erect and trailing. The difference is primarily in the character of the canes. Erect berries have arched, self-supporting canes; the trailing blackberries, also called dewberries, have canes that run on the ground. They should be supported on poles or trellises in cultivation. Trailing blackberries are normally larger, sweeter and ripen earlier.

Site location

In selecting the site for blackberries, look for a well drained location. Also, blackberries planted on hillsides are less likely to be damaged by winter weather and spring frost.

Soil

Most soils are suitable for growing blackberries; the moisture in the soil is the most important factor. While berries are growing and ripening, the blackberry plants need a large supply of water; however, the plants are harmed if water is allowed to stand around their roots.

Planting

Preparing to plant

Plant blackberries in early spring in the North and late winter or early spring in the South. Plow and work the soil the same as for a garden. Disk and harrow the soil just before setting out the plants.

Plant the erect varieties 5 feet apart in rows 8 feet apart (1,090 plants per acre). Set the trailing varieties 8 feet apart in rows 10 feet apart (545 plants per acre).

Planting the berries

1. When you receive the plants, set them out as soon as possible. Do not let the plants dry out. If the plants have started to dry out, soak them in water for a few hours. If you can't plant them immediately, "heel them in" to protect the

roots. To "heel in," dig a trench deep enough to contain the roots, then spread the plants along the trench, roots down, and cover them with moist soil.

2. Before setting the plants, cut the tops back so they are about 6 inches long.
3. Dip the roots in a thin slurry of mud to help protect them.
4. Make a planting hole by cutting a slit in the soil with the blade of a mattock or shovel. Press the handle forward to open the hole.
5. Set the blackberry plant about the same depth it was growing.
6. Withdraw the tool and press the dirt firmly around the plant with the heel.
7. If the soil is dry, water the plants as they are set out.
8. Then firm the soil around the roots of the plants.
9. Don't intergrow crops with blackberries after the first year. However, the first year you can grow beans, peas and other similar cultivated crops between the rows. Once blackberry plants reach bearing size, they need all the nutrients and moisture from the soil for satisfactory production.

Training and Pruning

Blackberry plants should be trained to run on trellises. Erect varieties can be grown without a trellis, but many canes will be broken during cultivation and harvesting.

Training

1. To make a trellis, stretch wire between posts set 15 to 20 feet apart in the row.
2. For erect varieties, use a single wire attached to the posts about 30 inches from the ground. For semi-trailing and trailing varieties, use 2 wires, one about 30 inches from the ground and the other about 50 inches from the ground.
3. Tie the canes to the wire with soft string. Tie the erect varieties where the canes cross the wires. Tie the trailing varieties horizontally along the wires. Spread them out to grow in both directions. Avoid tying in bundles.

Pruning

One of the most important items in managing blackberry plants is proper pruning. The crowns of the blackberries are perennial; new canes arise from them each year. The canes are biennial;

they live only 2 years. During the first year, they grow and send out branches. In the second year, buds from these branches grow and the fruit is borne on these buds. After the plant fruits, that cane dies and should be removed during the summer and burned.

Use the following procedure to prune your blackberries.

1. Prune the laterals back to about 18 inches early in the spring before growth starts. Fruit from pruned laterals is larger and of better quality.
2. Erect blackberries send up root suckers, in addition to new canes, during the growing season. Pull out all suckers that appear between the rows.
3. When the canes reach a height of about 36 inches, cut off the tips. This makes the canes branch to give better support to a heavy fruit crop.
4. The erect varieties should have 3 or 4 canes after pruning; trailing varieties about 8 to 10 canes.

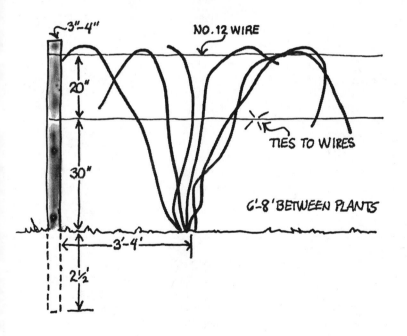

Soil Management

Cultivation
Blackberry plants should be cultivated thoroughly and frequently. Keep weeds and grass out of the plants. Start cultivating early in the spring and continue during the growing season. Plow

only 1 or 2 inches deep next to the plants to avoid harming the shallow roots.

Cover crops
Winter cover crops of small grains and clover help to prevent soil erosion and add humus to the soil. Plow the cover crops under in the early spring.

Fertilizing
The berry plants should have an application of 5-10-5 commercial fertilizer every year at blossoming time, and a second application after the fruit is harvested. Apply the fertilizer at the rate of 5 to 10 pounds per 50 feet of row. Use ammonium nitrate in the second application at the rate of 80 to 100 pounds per acre.

Propagating
Blackberry plants are easy to propagate. Most growers start their own planting stock.

The best way to start erect blackberry plants is by root cuttings planted in the location where they are to fruit. Dig root pieces, at least 1/4 inch in diameter, from around established plants in early spring. Cut the roots into 3 inch lengths and bury them in trenches 2 or 3 inches deep.

Propagate trailing varieties in summer by loosening the soil around the plants and burying the tips of the canes about 3 inches deep, pointing the tips straight down. Always propagate thornless varieties in this manner to insure that the plant stays thornless.

Pollination
Some varieties of blackberries require cross-pollination, so it is a good idea to plant more than one variety. Even self-pollinated varieties may benefit. The flowers of blackberries are very attractive to bees, who are the chief pollinator. Honeybees should be placed around large acreages to insure proper pollination.

Harvesting
Firm, ripe blackberries bring the highest prices. The berries should be picked at the proper time, handled carefully and stored in

a cool place. Pick the berries as soon as they become sweet. They should be fully ripe, but firm. Most varieties should be picked every other day after they start ripening.

In the large commercial growing areas, berries are machine harvested, but you will probably not have enough acreage to justify machine harvesting.

Insects and Diseases

Blackberries are comparatively free from diseases and insects. Where diseases are found in the area, select varieties that are resistant to such diseases as orange rust, anthracnose and leaf spot. Blackberries are susceptible to verticillium wilt, which is a soil-borne fungus. Plant resistant varieties in areas where wilt is a problem.

Varieties

To get the greatest yield and best quality berries, choose types and varieties that are adapted to your area.

Well-managed berries will yield from 5000 to 6000 pounds per acre, sometimes more. The following description of the major varieties should help you select blackberries best suited for your particular area. The date of maturity is indicated for each variety; however, it is difficult to apply a set standard for ripening for each variety in different sections of the country because of the variables caused by time, the characteristics of the berries, the zone and area adaptation, and the disease susceptibility.

Erect Varieties
1. **Alfred.** Early ripening. Berries large, firm, sweet. Bushes hardy, vigorous and productive. Adapt to northern states, especially Michigan.

2. **Bailey.** Midseason ripening. Large fruit, glossy black. Tall bushes and vigorous, hardy and productive. New York area.

3. **Brazos.** Early ripening. Fruit is large and fairly firm; very productive and vigorous. Texas and Gulf Coast area.

4. **Dallas.** Ripens early. Berries large and firm; vine semi-trailing, hardy, vigorous and productive. Especially adapted to Texas and Oklahoma.

5. **Darrow.** Early ripening; long fruiting season. Berries glossy black, large, firm, mildly acid. Bushes very hardy and productive. New England area.

6. **Early Harvest.** Early long fruiting season. Medium-sized berries. Bushes moderately erect, vigorous, very productive for upper south. Grown as far north as Maryland and southern Illinois.

7. **Eldorado.** Early to midseason; long fruiting season. Berries medium to large, firm, sweet. Bushes hardy, productive and very vigorous. Not adapted to the extreme south. Most resistant to orange rust of widely grown varieties.

8. **Flint:** Midseason; prolonged ripening. Berries large and firm with a good flavor. Plants productive. Adapted to the South and Southwest. Plant resistant to leaf spot and anthracnose.

9. **Hedrick.** Early ripening. Berries large, glossy and firm. Bushes hardy, productive, and vigorous. New England. Susceptible to orange rust.

10. **Himalaya.** Late maturing. Medium-sized berries, rather soft and sweet. Good producer. West Coast.

11. **Lawton.** Midseason ripening. Berries are large, soft, and sweet. Bushes vigorous and productive. Grown in Texas and Oklahoma.

12. **Smoothstem.** Very late in ripening. Berries are large, firm, tart, and with good flavor. Canes are thornless. Grows well along the Atlantic Coast and is good for home gardens. Resistant to leaf spot.

13. **Thornfree.** Late ripening. Berries large, firm, tart, and very good. Canes thornless. Hardy from central New Jersey south and in the Pacific Northwest. Resistant to leaf spot.

Trailing Varieties.

1. **Advance.** Very early ripening. Large, firm berries. Grown in southern California and Florida. Very resistant to rosette.

2. **Boysen.** Late ripening. Berries are very large, tart, high flavored, and soft. Widely grown in the South and Pacific Coast.

3. **Cascade.** Early ripening. The berries are bright, deep red and have excellent flavor. Plant vigorous and productive. Grown in western Oregon and Washington.

4. **Flordagrand.** Very early ripening. Berries large, glossy, soft, and aromatic. Bushes vigorous and disease resistant. Requires cross-pollination. Best adapted along the Gulf Coast.

5. **Logan.** Early ripening. Large, long dark red berries. Plants are vigorous and highly productive. Not adapted to the East Coast.

6. **Mayes.** Early ripening. Large, soft berries. Plants vigorous and productive. Texas' leading variety. Susceptible to anthracnose and rosette.

7. **Oklawaha.** Very early ripener. Medium-sized berry, but with good flavor. Florida and Gulf Coast area.

8. **Olallie.** Ripens midseason. The berries are large, firm and bright black. The plants are vigorous and productive. Adapted to California, Oregon and the Gulf Coast.

9. **Young.** Berries ripen in midseason. The berries are wine colored, very large and very sweet. The plants are vigorous. Do best in the South and Pacific Coast.

Blueberries

The blueberry is a shrub in the heath family. It produces small blue berries that can be eaten fresh with cream or sugar or made into delicious tarts, pies and other pastries.

Blueberries have been cultivated commercially for a relatively short period of time. However, they are steadily gaining in popularity as more varieties are developed for growing in areas where the original wild blueberries and the early cultivated species would not grow.

Blueberry varieties have been developed by hybridization and breeding of native wild species. This breeding has produced cultivated blueberries that are sweeter and about three times the size of the largest wild berries. The cultivated varieties are superior to the wild ones for marketing fresh because of their larger size and better appearance.

The two cultivated species are the highbush and rabbiteye. The highbush are raised from southeastern North Carolina to southern Maine and west to southern Michigan. The rabbiteye blueberries are raised in southern Georgia, southern Alabama, northern Florida, and as far west as Arkansas and the eastern section of Texas.

Planning and Preparation

Soil

Cultivated blueberries grow best where the soil is very acid and moist, although the rabbiteye varieties are not as sensitive to soil type and are far more resistant to heat and drought than the highbush varieties. The best indication that blueberries may grow successfully in a particular kind of soil is if they, or some related plants such as huckleberries, azaleas or laurel, are growing there naturally. Open, porous soils of sand and peat that contain some loam and that have a water table 14 to 30 inches below the surface are best for blueberries. The plants are not hardy in temperatures lower than –20° F.

For best results in growing blueberries, the pH of the soil should be from 4.3 to 4.8; however, good growth may occur in soils with a pH as low as 4.0. To be safe, apply ground magnesium limestone to bring the soil pH up to 4.5. Where the soil pH is as high as 5.5, use finely ground sulfur or ammonium sulfate.

Temperature

Weather conditions affect the flavor and other characteristics of the fruit. Generally, the berries are better flavored toward the northern limits of the growing area where the nights are cool during the ripening season. Highbush varieties begin to ripen the latter part of May in northern Georgia, the last of June in New Jersey, and mid July in Massachusetts and Maine. The rabbiteye blueberries have better flavor when the days are sunny and the nights cool. They will start to ripen in May and will continue for about a month. They ripen over a longer period than highbush varieties.

Planting

Because cross pollination by honeybees is necessary for maximum production of all commercial varieties of blueberries, plant at least two varieties. Bees increase the number of berries set and shorten the ripening period.

Use the following procedure when you plant your blueberries.
1. Set highbush varieties 4 to 5 feet apart in rows that are spaced 9 to 10 feet apart. Space rabbiteye varieties 6 to 12 feet apart in rows spaced 12 feet apart. Start as early in the spring as the soil can be worked.
2. Set the blueberry plants on a well-prepared bed at the same depth they were growing in the nursery.
3. Dig the hole large enough and deep enough to spread the roots in the hole without crowding them.
4. Press the dirt firmly around the roots.
5. Water the plants if the soil is the least bit dry. Use water to settle the dirt around the roots.

Pruning

To produce good berries, the blueberry bush should be pruned. The largest fruit is borne on the most vigorous wood of the previous season's growth. Usually very little pruning is necessary until the end of the third season, when regular annual pruning should begin. The general practice is as follows:
1. Cut out the low spreading branches next to the ground. Leave only the more erect branches or shoots.
2. If the center of the bush is dense, cut out the weak and older branches at the center.
3. Remove most of the slender branches, leaving strong branches and shoots.

Soil Management

Irrigation

Blueberries are not drought resistant. Even in areas where they do best, you will need to irrigate if you want to be successful raising them.

Cultivation

The blueberry plant is shallow rooted; therefore, cultivation should be shallow. Deep plowing will cut feeder roots. Keep the ground free of weeds and grass.

Cover crops

Use cover crops between the rows during the winter.

BEFORE PRUNING

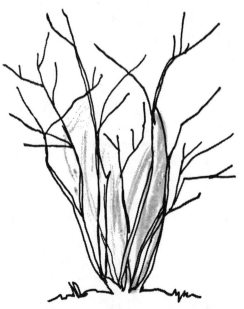

SAME BUSH AFTER PRUNING

Fertilizing

Under favorable conditions, productive bushes will require heavy fertilizer applications — as much as 600 pounds per acre of a complete fertilizer such as 10-20-10 or 8-12-8. In addition, a month or so later apply 100 pounds of ammonium sulfate per acre.

Propagating

Highbush varieties

1. Propagate these varieties by hardwood cuttings, 4 to 5 inches long.
2. Make the cuttings from dormant shoots of the previous season's growth when the plants are dormant.
3. Make the lower cut just below a bud and the upper cut just above a bud. Cut off and discard wood with fruit buds because these cuttings do not root satisfactorily.
4. Store the cuttings in a cool, moist place until they can be set in the propagating trays in early spring.
5. The most commonly used trays are 6 feet long, 27 inches wide and 4 inches deep. The bottom is made of 1/8-inch to 1/4-inch wire mesh hardware cloth.
6. Fill the trays with peat or peat and sand.
7. Place the cuttings in a slant position about 1 inch apart in rows 2 inches apart.

Rabbiteye varieties

Propagate these varieties by offshoots or suckers. They can be started from softwood cuttings; hardwood cuttings root very poorly from rabbiteye varieties.

Harvesting

The dense thick bushes are the hardest to pick the fruit from. The bush should be opened up to allow sunlight in and to enable the picker to gather the fruit. To increase the size of the fruit, prune back the shoots depending on the number of fruit buds on the shoots. Cutting back is usually done after danger of cold weather is over. The pruning itself can be done any time in the late fall or winter. Rabbiteye varieties should be pruned enough to prevent the bushes from becoming too dense.

Insects and Diseases

The most common insects attacking blueberries are the blueberry maggot, cranberry fruitworm, blueberry bud mite, plum curculio and the cranberry weevil.

Blueberry maggot

The adult blueberry maggot is similar to a housefly in shape. It is about 3/16 inch long, has a brown face and a shiny black body with several white bands on the abdomen. Its wings are clear with black bands. The larvae are whitish-yellow maggots about 3/8 inch long. The maggots puncture the skin of the berries and feed on the flesh, causing the berries to collapse, wither, and drop from the bush.

The blueberry maggot is prevalent from New Jersey northward. Ask your local nursery man for information concerning insecticides that are available for use in controlling the blueberry maggot. Carefully follow directions on the container.

Cranberry fruitworm

The adult moths of the cranberry fruitworm appear during late May and early June. They lay their eggs in the calyx cup at the base of newly set fruit. The larvae are greenish on their sides and undersides, and brownish red on their backs. They are about 1/2 inch long. The green berries are attacked by these larvae, and they will destroy a large number of berries if not controlled.

This insect is found in all areas from Maine to Texas. Malathion or carbaryl, applied three times at 10 day intervals just after petal fall, usually provides control.

Blueberry bud mite

This tiny, soft-bodied mite with eight legs sucks juices from the buds. This distorts the flowers so they fail to set fruit. The berries may only partially develop and the skin may be rough. Red, blistered and misshapen berries are the first signs of infestation.

This mite is a serious pest in North Carolina and to a lesser extent in New Jersey. The application of endosulfan mixed with water immediately after harvest, and repeated 6 to 8 weeks later should provide control. Do not apply endosulfan after the buds are well formed.

Plum curculio

The adults of the plum curculio are dark brown beetles with grayish or whitish patches on their backs and four humps on their wing covers. They are about 1/4 inch long. The larvae are grayish white, with small brown heads and legless curved bodies. They are

BLUEBERRY MAGGOT

PLUM CURCULIO

about 1/3 inch long. The adults appear early in the blooming period, feed and lay their eggs in the small green berries. Usually there is one larva in each berry. The larvae feed on the fruit, causing the fruit to drop.

This insect is found east of the Rocky Mountains, and can be controlled by spraying. Ask your nursery man for information concerning available sprays and carefully follow directions on the container.

Cranberry weevil

This insect is a dark reddish-brown with white patches across its wings. It is about 1/3 inch long and has a slightly curved snout one-third as long as the rest of its body. The larvae have a whitish, legless body about 1/9 inch long and a yellow head. The adult weevils bore into the leaf and fruit buds and eat the flesh. When the blossoms start turning white, the weevils lay their eggs in the flower. After the larvae hatch, they eat the entire contents of the flower, thus severely limiting production.

84 These weevils are found east of the Rocky Mountains and are best controlled by keeping the area clean. This can be accomplished through cultivation and by burning trash and dry weeds off adjacent areas in the spring before buds begin to swell. Either of these methods will kill off the hibernating weevils.

Diseases

There are a large number of fungus, viral and bacterial diseases that affect blueberries with stem canker. This causes the most damage over-all, followed by foliage diseases, stunt virus, stem blight and phytophthora root rot. Contact your local county agent for information on the diseases that are prevalent in your area and the best methods of control.

Varieties

Of the principal varieties grown, the best for western North Carolina, Maryland and New Jersey are Bluetta, Collins, Blueray, Bluecrop, Berkeley, Jersey and Lateblue. In eastern North Carolina, the most important varieties are Morrow, Wolcott, Murphy and Croatan. In Michigan and New England, the best varieties are Jersey, Bluecrop, Earliblue, Blueray, Collins, Coville and Lateblue. In western Oregon and Washington, the most commonly grown varieties are Bluecrop, Dixi, Collins, Blueray, Berkeley, Herbert, Darrow and Coville. In the southern part of the country the rabbiteye varieties that are most commonly grown are Woodard, Tifblue, Delite and Southland.

Highbush varieties

1. **Berkeley.** Bush vigorous, spreading, productive; leaf large. Fruit cluster loose; berry very large, light blue, firm with slight aroma. Less acid than most varieties, good flavor, scar small. Stores well. Resistant to cracking. Late midseason ripening.

2. **Bluecrop.** Bush medium, vigor hardy, productive, upright. Fruit large, firm, light blue, small scar. Mild flavor. Tight cluster. Ripens in midseason.

3. **Blueray.** Bush very vigorous, upright, hardy, productive. Fruit cluster small, tight; berry very large, light blue, firm. Resistant to cracking. Excellent flavor, aromatic. Scar medium-sized. Ripens in midseason.

4. **Bluetta.** Bush of medium vigor, spreading, productive. Fruit medium-sized, firm, light blue color, good flavor. Early variety for New Jersey and Michigan.

5. **Collins.** Bush vigorous, upright, moderately productive. Fruit clusters medium tight, attractive; berry large, firm, light blue. Excellent flavor. Early midseason ripening.

85

6. **Coville.** Bush vigorous, spreading, productive, leaf large. Fruit cluster loose, berry very large, light blue, firm, aromatic. Good flavor but tart till ripe. Ripens late. Does not drop.

7. **Croatan.** Bush vigorous, spreading, productive, leaf large. Fruit cluster loose, berry medium to large, dark blue, medium firm. Slightly aromatic. Good flavor. Scar very small.

8. **Darrow.** Bush erect, vigorous, productive. Fruit cluster medium-sized, berry large, light blue, firm. Tart until fully ripe, excellent flavor.

9. **Dixi.** Bush vigorous, spreading, productive, leaf large. Fruit cluster medium tight, berry large, blue, firm, aromatic. Excellent flavor. Subject to cracking. Scar large.

10. **Earliblue.** Bush vigorous, upright, productive. Fruit cluster loose, berry large, light blue, firm. Resistant to cracking. Aromatic, good flavor. Scar small. Early variety.

11. **Herbert.** Bush vigorous, upright, productive. Fruit cluster loose, berry very large, medium firm, medium blue. Resistant to cracking. Aromatic, excellent flavor. Scar size medium.

12. **Jersey.** Bush vigorous, erect, productive, leaf large. Fruit cluster long and loose, berry medium-sized, light blue, firm, no aroma. Fair flavor. Scar small.

13. **Lateblue.** Bush moderately vigorous, upright, productive. Fruit cluster loose, large leaf, berry medium large, firm. Good flavor. Scar medium. Ripens late with many berries ripe at the same time.

14. **Morrow.** Bush spreading, slow growing. Berries large, medium blue. Good flavor, medium firm. Ripens earliest of all varieties.

15. **Murphy.** Bush vigorous, spreading, productive, leaf large. Fruit cluster loose, berry medium-sized, dark blue, firm. Slightly aromatic, fair flavor. Scar medium.

16. **Wolcott.** Bush very vigorous, upright, productive, leaf large. Fruit cluster loose, berry medium-sized, dark blue, firm, aromatic. Good flavor. Small scar.

Rabbiteye varieties

1. **Delite.** Bush vigorous, medium size. Fruit medium-sized, flavor excellent. Color medium dark, medium firm. Good yield. Late season ripening.

2. **Southland.** Bush medium-sized. Fruit firm, berries medium-sized. Flavor fair, color medium blue. Yield average. Midseason ripening.

3. **Tifblue.** Large bush, vigorous, large berries, light blue, firm. Good flavor. High yields. Midseason ripening.

4. **Woodard.** Small vigorous bush, large berries, light blue color, medium firm. Excellent flavor. High yields. Early season ripening.

Raspberries

Raspberries are a popular, tasty cane fruit related to the blackberry — both are members of the genus *Rubus* of the rose family. The raspberry is used in pies, desserts, sherbets, jellies and preserves.

While the areas in which raspberries are grown commercially are rather limited, they can be grown successfully for home use and small commercial operations by careful irrigation, mulching and other practices. The important commercial growing areas include Western Maryland, southern New Jersey, the Hudson River Valley, western New York, western Michigan, southern Minnesota, the Puyallup Valley of Washington and the Willamette Valley of Oregon.

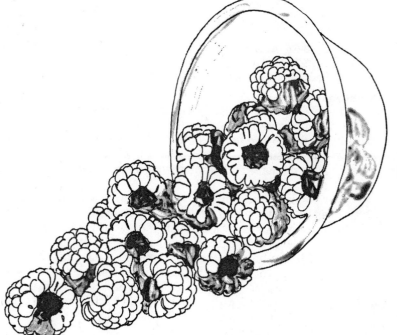

Planning and Preparation

Raspberries' natural growing areas are in places with a mild climate, especially in the summer. They can not tolerate hot, dry weather for a long period of time. The raspberry does well where the soil is moist but well drained, loamy and rich in humus. The summer temperatures should not consistently stay above 90°F.

There are two main classes or types of cultivated raspberries, distinct both in growth and in fruiting characteristics: the red raspberry and the black raspberry. The red raspberry produces many slender, upright, unbranched shoots and spreads rapidly by means of sucker plants. The black raspberry produces new plants by tip layers. The tips are buried about 2 inches deep in late summer, and the rooted tips are dug up early the next spring. These tips root freely when they are in contact with the soil.

From a 30-foot row of raspberries properly cared for, you can harvest all the fresh fruit a family of five can eat during the bearing season, and have some left for jam and jelly or freezing to keep for the winter.

Planting

Preparing to plant

It is best to plant raspberries in the early spring after a clean cultivated crop.

1. Prepare the soil by plowing and disking. Be sure the soil is well drained as raspberries can not tolerate wet ground.
2. Select good strong healthy plants.

Planting the berries

1. For red raspberries, space the rows 8 feet apart and the plants 2 feet apart in the row.
2. Set plants into holes so the growing points are an inch below the surface. These will bear a full crop 2 years later. New shoots from the roots will fill in the row between the plants.
3. For black and purple raspberries, space the rows 6 feet apart and the plants 3 feet apart in the row.
4. Dig a hole and spread out the roots so the main growth bud is 2 inches below the ground line. Refill with soil. Plants will bear a full crop the second year after planting.
5. Use stakes or trellises to prevent wind damage and to make harvest easier. A 2-wire trellis has proved most satisfactory. Space the wires about 24 inches apart, one on each side of the row, about 3 feet high.
6. Tie the canes to the wires.

Pruning

Pruning is essential to maintaining raspberries. Shoots produced in the spring and summer bear fruit the following year and then die. You must cut away these canes each year just after harvest to make room for the new shoots. Burning dead and cut canes is an important measure to prevent disease and insect problems. Remove the canes from the area when they're burned.

Pruning the black raspberry
1. The black raspberry requires summer topping. Break out the top 4 inches of the new shoot when it reaches a height of 24 to 28 inches. This will cause faster lateral development and stronger plants.
2. Shorten the laterals to a length of 8 to 10 inches in the spring before growth starts.

Pruning the red raspberry
1. Do not summer top the red raspberry.
2. Prune it in the spring prior to growth to limit the number of canes.
3. Shorten the remaining canes sufficiently to support the weight of the crop. The stouter the canes of both black and red raspberries, the more productive they are.

Soil Management

Cultivation
Clean cultivation is usually practiced. The cultivation should be shallow so as not to damage the feeder roots of the plants. Cultivate often enough to keep down weeds and grass.

Cover crops
Plant winter cover crops in areas that do not have winter snow cover. This will protect the soil and add humus.

Mulching and irrigating

Mulch where possible to conserve moisture, prevent weed growth and reduce summer soil temperature. If necessary, irrigate to keep the soil moist.

Fertilizing
Apply fertilizer annually to maintain high production: 2500 to 3000 quarts per acre of red raspberries and 2000 to 2500 quarts per acre of black raspberries. Most soil will need approximately 800 to 1000 pounds of 10-20-10 per acre. Apply it each spring, half on each side of the row in bands about 18 to 24 inches wide. Barnyard manure is very helpful in that it also supplies much needed humus to the soil.

Harvesting

The fruits are clusters of small drupelets attached to the plant by a torus. Unless the berry will separate from the torus, it is not ripe and should not be picked. The raspberry has a flavor that is complex and delicate only when fully ripe.

1. To pick ripe raspberries, grasp each berry gently between thumb and fingers and pull it from the plant, leaving the torus or white core on the stem.
2. Use small containers so berries won't be crushed by their own weight.
3. Don't wash berries until you are ready to eat them.

Diseases

A planting properly cared for should last at least 10 years. Most plantings last a shorter span due in most part to one or more of the following diseases.

Viral diseases
The most serious problems are created by a group of viral diseases: leaf curl, mosaic and streak. These diseases cannot be controlled by spraying or by other conventional methods, but must be avoided by planting stock certified to be free from these diseases. Should any plant show signs of these diseases, remove it immediately. Although there are differences in susceptibility between varieties and species, all raspberries appear to be affected.

Anthracnose
This disease, a major problem in some areas, attacks the stems and canes and causes lesions. It can be controlled by means of a liquid-lime sulfur spray applied in early spring, followed by sprays of ferbam and captan.

Other diseases
90 Raspberries are also affected by crown gall and verticillium wilt. These organisms are soil related and can be avoided by selecting planting sites free from the diseases.

Varieties

Black raspberry varieties
1. **Cumberland.** An old-time, reliable, midseason variety of good quality, size and flavor.
2. **Black Hawk.** A heavy, midseason producer of excellent fruit.

3. **Morrison.** A large late variety that is relatively seedless.

4. **Bristol, New Logan, Shuttleworth** and **Plum Farmer** are also good black varieties.

Purple raspberry varieties

1. **Columbia.** A high yielding tart variety.

2. **Sodus.** A large, firm, purple berry that ripens over a long period.

3. **Burgundy Purple.** A high yielding kind that is strongly disease-resistant.

Golden or Amber raspberry varieties

Golden Queen. Bears in June. A delicious and sweet flavor.

Red raspberry varieties

1. **Latham.** A hardy, midseason variety that is a standard for the red varieties.

2. **Indian Summer.** Produces early and repeats again in the fall. Sometimes known as ever-bearing because of its two crop production.

3. **September.** Another of the repeat-bearing kind. Non-crumbling and very flavorful. Has large-sized berries.

4. **Willamette.** Grown mostly on the West Coast.

5. **Sunrise.** A very early variety that produces heavily and has good fruit.

6. **Taylor.** A good variety for the East. May be very tart.

Glossary

Anthers
That part of a flower that develops and contains pollen.
Arms
The growth of grape vines that has the buds and produces the fruit.
Axils
The part of the plant that is the angle between a branch or leaf and the trunk or limb.
Balling hydrometer
An instrument with a ball that floats in a tube and shows the sugar content of the liquid by determining the specific gravity.
Buds
The bulge on the stem that develops into a flower or leaf.
Canes
The limbs of berry plants.
Catkins
The male flower that produces pollen on nut trees.
Cordon
A protective cover.
Crowns
The parts of plants that take root and establish additional plants at a point where stem and root merge.
Cultivars
Varieties that are cultivated instead of allowed to grow wild.
Dichogamy
A plant that produces separate male and female flowers and usually at different times.
Dormant
The period when a perennial plant is at rest (as in the winter).
Foxy
A berry that has a sharp, brisk flavor and aroma.
Galls
Swellings of plant tissue that produce roundish hard knots.
Gumbo
A heavy, sticky, gummy soil with a high clay content.

Harrow
To cultivate lightly so as to destroy small weeds, pulverize clods and smooth the soil.
Hybrid
A plant that is produced by using two different varieties as parents.
Lateral buds
Buds that develop in the axil between a petiole and a stem; also called axillary buds.
Long-cane pruning
A system of pruning that leaves more than the usual amount of buds on the arms of a vine that is a heavy producer.
Medium-cane pruning
Normal pruning.
Nodes
The joints on a vine.
Nut kernel percentage
The percentage of meat in a nut as compared with the hull.
pH.
A scale used to indicate the concentration of hydrogen ions in the soil to determine if the soil is acid or alkaline.
Pistil
The ovule-bearing organ of the flower.
Pistillate
A flower that has pistils but no stamens.
Precocious
The ability to produce fruit or nuts at an early age.
Propagation
To increase the number of a variety by seeding, budding and grafting.
Protandrous
A dichogamous plant that produces the catkin and pollen first.
Protogynous
A dichogamous plant that produces the female flower first.
Refractometer

An instrument to measure the deflection of light rays.
Renewal spurs
Buds that are allowed to develop to replace canes that have produced and are to be removed.
Rootstock
The roots and that part of the plant below a graft.
Runners
Long stems or canes that establish crowns or plants at nodes on the stems.
Self-fertilizing
A plant that has flowers that are capable of pollinating themselves.

Shoots
New growth that is not mature.
Short-cane pruning
The practice of pruning canes so that they only have a few buds.
Spurs
Horny or stubby growths next to the trunk or limbs.
Staminate
Flowers that have a stamen but no pistils.
Stigma
The part of the pistil of the flower that receives the pollen.
Suckers
A shoot from the roots or lower stem of a plant.
Tendrils
A slender coiling part of the plant that attaches to supports to help hold the vine in place.
Trunk
The main part of the tree that supports the limbs.

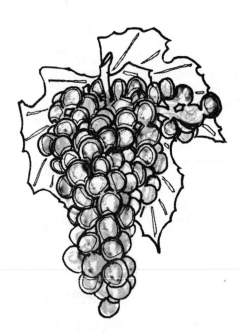

Countryside Gardening Books
Little Book Series
5½ by 8 inch format

INDOOR ASSORTMENT

Cactus & Succulents (101)
Herb Gardening (102)
Foliage Houseplants (103)
Flowering Houseplants (104)
Vines & Ivy (106)
Ferns & Palms (107)
African Violets (108)
Orchids (111)
Houseplant Handcrafts (114)
Houseplant Multiplying (117)
Don't Throw it Away . . . Plant it (118)
Houseplant RX (119)
Greenhouse Gardening (126)

OUTDOOR ASSORTMENT

Container Planting (105)
Geraniums (109)
Begonias (110)
Garden Bulbs (112)
Correct Planting Methods (113)
Vegetable Gardening (115)
Entice Birds to Your Garden (116)
Shade Trees (120)
Evergreens (121)
Groundcovers, Vines & Hedges (122)
Annuals & Perennials (123)
Better Lawns (124)
Rose Handbook (125)

Large Books
8¼ by 10½ inch format

SIX WAYS TO GROW HOUSEPLANTS, (201)
 by Muriel Orans, 265 color photos, **$3.95**
NEW IDEAS IN FLOWER GARDENING, (202)
 by Derek Fell, 225 color photos, **$3.95**
LOOK, MOM, IT'S GROWING, (203)
 by Ed Fink, illustrated children's book, **$2.95**
HOUSEPLANTS AND INDOOR LANDSCAPING, (204)
 by Muriel Orans, 248 color photos, **$3.95**
HOW TO PLANT A VEGETABLE GARDEN, (205)
 by Derek Fell, 100 color photos, **$3.95**
HOME LANDSCAPING, (206)
 over 500 color photos, **$5.95**
BONSAI AND THE JAPANESE GARDEN, (207)
 by Domoto & Kay, 85 color photos, **$3.95**
RAISE VEGETABLES, FRUITS & HERBS IN CONTAINERS, (208)
 by "Doc" & Katy Abraham, **$2.95**

95

Countryside
Books

A. B. Morse Co.
200 James St., Barrington, Ill. 60010